Healthy Lives, Healthy People: Our strategy for public health in England

Presented to Parliament by
the Secretary of State for Health
by Command of Her Majesty
30 November 2010

CM7985

Any enquiries regarding this publication should be sent to us at publichealthengland@dh.gsi.gov.uk

This publication is also available on http://www.official-documents.gov.uk/

ISBN: 9780101798525

Printed in the UK for The Stationery Office Limited on behalf of the Controller of Her Majesty's Stationery Office

ID 2402519   11/10

Printed on paper containing 75% recycled fibre content minimum.

Contents

Foreword

This White Paper outlines a radical shift in the way we tackle public health challenges. We have to be bold because so many of the lifestyle-driven health problems we see today are already at alarming levels.

Britain is now the most obese nation in Europe. We have among the worst rates of sexually transmitted infections recorded, a relatively large population of problem drug users and rising levels of harm from alcohol. Smoking alone claims over 80,000 lives every year. Experts estimate that tackling poor mental health could reduce our overall disease burden by nearly a quarter. Health inequalities between rich and poor have been getting progressively worse. We still live in a country where the wealthy can expect to live longer than the poor.

The dilemma for government is this: it is simply not possible to promote healthier lifestyles through Whitehall diktat and nannying about the way people should live. Recent years have proved that one-size-fits-all solutions are no good when public health challenges vary from one neighbourhood to the next. But we cannot sit back while, in spite of all this, so many people are suffering such severe lifestyle-driven ill health and such acute health inequalities.

We need a new approach that empowers individuals to make healthy choices and gives communities the tools to address their own, particular needs. The plans set out in this White Paper put local communities at the heart of public health. We will end central control and give local government the freedom, responsibility and funding to innovate and develop their own ways of improving public health in their area. There will be real financial incentives to reward their progress on improving health and reducing health inequalities, and greater transparency so people can see the results they achieve.

We are simplifying the way we organise things nationally, too, with a dedicated new public health service – Public Health England – taking the place of the complex structures that exist today. The new dedicated service will support local innovation, help provide disease control and protection and spread information on the latest innovations from around the world.

All this will be supported by work with industry and other partners to promote healthy living. New practices and technologies are already revolutionising efforts to prevent sickness and improve health and well-being – from partnerships between the voluntary sector and employers to incentivise people to be more active, to new phone apps that help people lose weight. If we can direct the collective power of this diverse innovation towards a single national purpose, we believe we can make real progress.

The result of all this will be a much more innovative, integrated and dynamic approach to improving public health. Under our plans local innovation will replace central control. People and communities will drive directly the change we need to build a stronger, healthier Britain.

Secretary of State for Health

Executive Summary: Our strategy for public health in England

1. This is a new era for public health, with a higher priority and dedicated resources. This White Paper outlines our commitment to protecting the population from serious health threats; helping people live longer, healthier and more fulfilling lives; and improving the health of the poorest, fastest.

2. It responds to Professor Sir Michael Marmot's *Fair Society, Healthy Lives*[1] report and adopts its life course framework for tackling the wider social determinants of health. The new approach will aim to build people's self-esteem, confidence and resilience right from infancy – with stronger support for early years. It complements *A Vision for Adult Social Care: Capable Communities and Active Citizens*[2] in emphasising more personalised, preventive services that are focused on delivering the best outcomes for citizens and that help to build the Big Society.

3. The goal is a public health service that achieves excellent results, unleashing innovation and liberating professional leadership. This White Paper builds on *Equity and Excellence: Liberating the NHS*[3] to set out the overall principles and framework for making this happen.

4. Subject to Parliament, local government and local communities will be at the heart of improving health and wellbeing for their populations and tackling inequalities. A new integrated public health service – Public Health England – will be created to ensure excellence, expertise and responsiveness, particularly on health protection, where a national response is vital.

5. During 2011, the Department of Health will publish documents that build on this new approach, including on mental health, tobacco control, obesity, sexual health, pandemic flu preparedness, health protection and emergency preparedness, together with documents from other government departments addressing many of the wider determinants of health.

6. The proposals in this White Paper apply to England, but we will work closely with the Devolved Administrations on areas of shared interest.

Seizing opportunities for better health

7.   Public health has formidable achievements to its name: clean air and water, enhanced nutrition and mass immunisation have consigned many killer diseases to the history books. There are huge opportunities to go further and faster in tackling today's causes of premature death and illness. People living in the poorest areas will, on average, die 7 years earlier than people living in richer areas and spend up to 17 more years living with poor health. They have higher rates of mental illness; of harm from alcohol, drugs and smoking; and of childhood emotional and behavioural problems. Although infectious diseases now account for only 1 in 50 deaths, rates of tuberculosis and sexually transmitted infections (STIs) are rising and pandemic flu is still a threat.

8.   A fuller story on the health of England is set out in *Our Health and Wellbeing Today*, published to accompany this White Paper. The opportunity – and the challenge – is stark, for example:

   a. By improving maternal health, we could give our children a better start in life, reduce infant mortality and the numbers of low birth-weight babies.

   b. Taking better care of our children's health and development could improve educational attainment and reduce the risks of mental illness, unhealthy lifestyles, road deaths and hospital admissions due to tooth decay.

   c. Being in work leads to better physical and mental health, and we could save the UK up to £100 billion a year by reducing working-age ill health.[4]

   d. Changing adults' behaviour could reduce premature death, illness and costs to society, avoiding a substantial proportion of cancers, vascular dementias and over 30% of circulatory diseases; saving the NHS the £2.7 billion cost of alcohol abuse; and saving society the £13.9 billion a year spent on tackling drug-fuelled crime.

   e. We could prevent many of the yearly excess winter deaths – 35,000 in 2008/09 – through warmer housing, and prevent further deaths through full take-up of seasonal flu vaccinations.

A radical new approach

9.   The current approach and system is not up to the task of seizing these huge opportunities for better health and reduced inequalities in health. This White Paper sets out a radical new approach that will empower local communities, enable professional freedoms and unleash new ideas based on the evidence of what works, while ensuring that the country remains resilient to and mitigates against current and future health threats. It sets out how our approach will:

a.   protect the population from health threats – led by central government, with a strong system to the frontline;

b.   empower local leadership and encourage wide responsibility across society to improve everyone's health and wellbeing, and tackle the wider factors that influence it;

c.   focus on key outcomes, doing what works to deliver them, with transparency of outcomes to enable accountability through a proposed new public health outcomes framework;

d.   reflect the Government's core values of freedom, fairness and responsibility by strengthening self-esteem, confidence and personal responsibility; positively promoting healthy behaviours and lifestyles; and adapting the environment to make healthy choices easier; and

e.   balance the freedoms of individuals and organisations with the need to avoid harm to others, use a 'ladder' of interventions to determine the least intrusive approach necessary to achieve the desired effect and aim to make voluntary approaches work before resorting to regulation.

10.   This approach will: **reach across and reach out** – addressing the root causes of poor health and wellbeing, reaching out to the individuals and families who need the most support – and be:

• **responsive** – owned by communities and shaped by their needs;

• **resourced** – with ring-fenced funding and incentives to improve;

• **rigorous** – professionally-led, focused on evidence, efficient and effective; and

• **resilient** – strengthening protection against current and future threats to health.

Health and wellbeing throughout life

11. The Government is radically shifting power to local communities, enabling them to improve health throughout people's lives, reduce inequalities and focus on the needs of the local population. This White Paper highlights local innovation and outlines the cross-government framework that will enable local communities to reduce inequalities and improve health at key stages in people's lives, including:

   a. empowering local government and communities, which will have new resources, rights and powers to shape their environments and tackle local problems;

   b. taking a coherent approach to different stages of life and key transitions instead of tackling individual risk factors in isolation. Mental health will be a key element, and we will shortly publish a new mental health strategy;

   c. giving every child in every community the best start in life. We will do this through our continued commitment to reduce child poverty, by investing to increase health visitor numbers, doubling by 2015 the number of families reached through the Family Nurse Partnership programme, and refocusing Sure Start Children's Centres for those who need them most. An Olympic and Paralympic-style sports competition will be offered to all schools from 2012;

   d. making it pay to work through our comprehensive welfare reforms, creating new jobs through local growth and working with employers to unleash their potential as champions of public health;

   e. designing communities for active ageing and sustainability. We will make active ageing the norm rather than the exception, for example by building more Lifetime Homes, protecting green spaces and launching physical activity initiatives, including a £135 million Lottery investment in a Mass Participation and Community Sport legacy programme. We will protect and promote community ownership of green spaces and improve access to land so that people can grow their own food; and

   f. working collaboratively with business and the voluntary sector through the Public Health Responsibility Deal with five networks on food, alcohol, physical activity, health at work and behaviour change. We plan to launch the Deal in early 2011 and expect to be able to announce agreements on further reformulation of food to reduce salt; better information for consumers about food; and promotion of more socially responsible retailing and consumption of alcohol. It will also develop the Change4Life campaign, for example through the 'Great Swapathon', £250 million of partner-funded vouchers to make healthy lifestyle choices easier.

A new public health system with strong local and national leadership

12. To support this new approach and avoid the problems of the past, we need to reform the public health system. Localism will be at the heart of this system, with responsibilities, freedoms and funding devolved wherever possible; enhanced central powers will be taken where absolutely necessary, for example in areas such as emergency preparedness and health protection. Within this system:

   a. Directors of Public Health will be the strategic leaders for public health and health inequalities in local communities, working in partnership with the local NHS and across the public, private and voluntary sectors. The Government will shortly publish a response to the recent consultation on proposed new local statutory health and wellbeing boards to support collaboration across the NHS and local authorities in order to meet communities' needs as effectively as possible.

   b. A new, dedicated, professional public health service – Public Health England – will be set up as part of the Department of Health, which will strengthen the national response on emergency preparedness and health protection.

   c. There will be ring-fenced public health funding from within the overall NHS budget to ensure that it is not squeezed by other pressures, for example NHS finances, although this will still be subject to the running-cost reductions and efficiency gains that will be required across the system. Early estimates suggest that current spend on areas that are likely to be the responsibility of Public Health England could be over £4 billion.

   d. There will be ring-fenced budgets for upper-tier and unitary local authorities and a new health premium to reward them for progress made against elements of the proposed public health outcomes framework, taking into account health inequalities.

   e. The core elements of the new system will be set out in the forthcoming Health and Social Care Bill and will therefore be subject to Parliament's approval.

   f. The best evidence and evaluation will be used, supporting innovative approaches to behaviour change – with a new National Institute for Health Research (NIHR) School for Public Health Research and a Policy Research Unit on Behaviour and Health. There will be greater transparency, with data on health outcomes published nationally and locally.

   g. The Chief Medical Officer will have a central role in providing independent advice to the Secretary of State for Health and the Government on the population's health. He or she will be the leading advocate for public health within, across and beyond government, and will lead a professional network for all those responsible for commissioning or providing public health.

h. Public health will be part of the NHS Commissioning Board's (NHSCB) mandate, with public health support for NHS commissioning nationally and locally. There will be stronger incentives for GPs so that they play an active role in public health.

Making it happen

13. We are implementing our strategy to make early and substantial progress, so that we make a real difference to health from the earliest opportunity. Subject to the passage of the Health and Social Care Bill, the Government plans to:

    a. enable the creation of Public Health England, which will take on full responsibilities from 2012, including the formal transfer of functions and powers from the Health Protection Agency (HPA) and the National Treatment Agency for Substance Misuse (NTA);

    b. transfer local health improvement functions to local government, with ring-fenced funding allocated to local government from April 2013; and

    c. give local government new functions to increase local accountability and support integration and partnership working across social care, the NHS and public health.

14. The transition to Public Health England will be developed in alignment with changes to Primary Care Trusts (PCTs) and Strategic Health Authorities (SHAs), and the creation of the NHSCB. The detailed arrangements will be set out in a series of planning letters throughout the course of 2011.

15. To get the details of the new system right and ensure that it delivers significant improvements to the health of the population, we will be consulting on some elements. A number of consultation questions are set out in Chapter 4 and summarised in Chapter 5 of this White Paper, and we would welcome your views. The consultation on these questions closes on 8 March 2011.

16. The Department of Health has published a review of the regulation of public health professionals by Dr Gabriel Scally. A consultation question about this is in Chapter 4 of this White Paper. We would welcome views on this report.

17. Forthcoming consultation documents will set out the proposed public health outcomes framework, and funding and commissioning arrangements for public health.

1. Seizing opportunities for better health

Summary

Public health has formidable achievements to its name: clean air and water, enhanced nutrition and mass immunisation have consigned many killer diseases to the history books. There are huge opportunities to go further and faster in tackling today's causes of premature death and illness. People living in the poorest areas will, on average, die 7 years earlier than people living in richer areas and spend up to 17 more years living with poor health. They have higher rates of mental illness; of harm from alcohol, drugs and smoking; and of childhood emotional and behavioural problems. Although infectious diseases now account for only 1 in 50 deaths, rates of tuberculosis and sexually transmitted infections (STIs) are rising and pandemic flu is still a threat.

A fuller story on the health of England is set out in *Our Health and Wellbeing Today*, published to accompany this White Paper. The opportunity – and the challenge – is stark, for example:

- By improving maternal health, we could give our children a better start in life, reduce infant mortality and the numbers of low birth-weight babies.

- Taking better care of our children's health and development could improve educational attainment and reduce the risks of mental illness, unhealthy lifestyles, road deaths and hospital admissions due to tooth decay.

- Being in work leads to better physical and mental health, and we could save the UK up to £100 billion a year by reducing working-age ill health.[5]

- Changing adults' behaviour could reduce premature death, illness and costs to society, avoiding a substantial proportion of cancers, vascular dementias and over 30% of circulatory diseases; saving the NHS the £2.7 billion cost of alcohol abuse; and saving £13.9 billion a year, the societal cost related to drug-fuelled crime.

- We could prevent many of the yearly excess winter deaths – 35,000 in 2008/09 – through warmer housing, and prevent further deaths through full take-up of seasonal flu vaccinations.

Our health and wellbeing today

1.1   Today, people in England are healthier and are living longer than ever before, and
have levels of wellbeing that are as good as those in other European countries.
Most of the major advances in life expectancy over the last two centuries came
from public health rather than healthcare. Public health innovations have included
the establishment of clean water and sewage systems that radically reduced
infectious diseases; clean air acts that curbed the pollution that killed thousands
into the early 1950s; enhanced nutrition that has largely eliminated many birth
defects and once common conditions such as rickets; and mass immunisation
programmes that have consigned to the history books the infectious diseases that
once dominated death certificates.

What is public health?

The Faculty of Public Health defines public health as: The science and art of
promoting and protecting health and wellbeing, preventing ill health and prolonging
life through the organised efforts of society.

There are three domains of public health: health improvement (including people's
lifestyles as well as inequalities in health and the wider social influences of health),
health protection (including infectious diseases, environmental hazards and emergency
preparedness) and health services (including service planning, efficiency, audit and
evaluation).[6]

1.2   Infectious diseases now account for only 1 in 50 deaths.[7] However, tuberculosis
and STIs are rising, and pandemic flu remains a threat. We expect more people to
have long-standing illnesses in future, and common mental health disorders are on
the rise. Our causes of premature death are dominated by 'diseases of lifestyle',
where smoking, unhealthy diet, excess alcohol consumption and sedentary
lifestyles are contributory factors.

1.3   Health inequalities in life expectancy and disability-free life expectancy are large.
We know that a wide range of factors affect people's health throughout their
life and drive inequalities such as early years care, housing and social isolation.
Despite this, our health efforts focus much more on treatment than on the causes
of poor health. The NHS spends over £2.7 billion a year on treating smoking-
related illness,[8] but less than £150 million on smoking cessation.[9] The Government

will work to re-balance the focus on the causes of ill health and ensure that public health funding is prioritised and not squeezed by other pressures, for example NHS finances, though it will still be subject to the running-cost reductions and efficiency gains that will be required across the system.

1.4 The contrast between what we know about the causes of premature death and illness in our society and the domination of our attention and spending on secondary care represents a profound challenge to our policy and our society as a whole. At a population level, it is not better treatment, but prevention – both primary and secondary, including tackling the wider social factors that influence health – which is likely to deliver greater overall increases in healthy life expectancy.

1.5 In order to meet this challenge, we need to think in more integrated and innovative ways about how we can empower people and communities to make healthier choices in their lives. We need to focus efforts across society on these big opportunities. This is potentially one of the great challenges of our generation – how we can create a public health service, not just a national sickness service.

How healthy and well are we overall?

1.6 People in England are healthier and are living longer than ever. Overall, we enjoy safe air and water, and are well protected from environmental hazards. We also have systems in place to prepare for and respond to new threats such as pandemic flu. However, there are substantial inequalities in health across the country – as there are in other wealthy countries. Figure 1.1 illustrates the variation in mortality of people under 75 in England; further analysis of public health data shows that different areas face different challenges (for instance, the patterns in smoking-related deaths are not the same as those in alcohol-related deaths, which are again different from those in excess winter deaths).[10]

Figure 1.1: Mortality from all causes, persons aged under 75, 2006–08, by local authority

(directly age-standardised mortality)

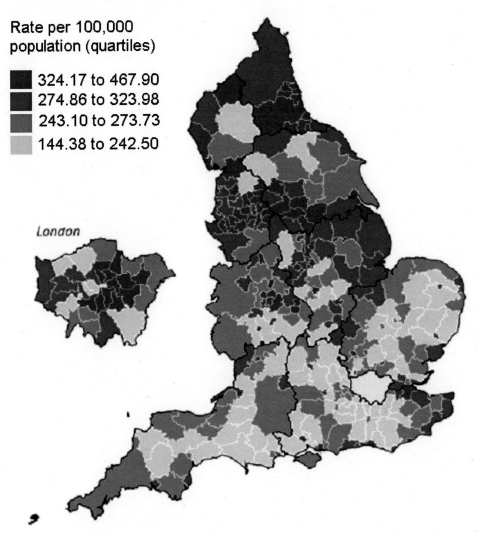

Rate per 100,000
population (quartiles)

- 324.17 to 467.90
- 274.86 to 323.98
- 243.10 to 273.73
- 144.38 to 242.50

London

Source: National Centre for Health Outcomes Development, Compendium of Clinical and Health Indicators.

1.7   Today, English men can expect to live until 78 – longer than in most other comparable nations; however, still not as long as English women, who can expect to live to 82.[11] Life expectancy is expected to continue to rise for both men and women, rising to 81 and 85 years of age respectively by 2020.[12]

1.8   However, many people are still dying at a relatively young age, with more than 1 in 6 deaths occurring before age 65 in 2007.[13] The leading causes of death across all ages are circulatory diseases, cancers and respiratory diseases, which together accounted for 75% of deaths in 2007.[14]

1.9   We know that people suffer a substantial burden of ill health from living with conditions that give them pain, affect their mental health, or prevent them from doing their usual activities, making them dependent on the care of others. The good news is that although we are living longer, there is no strong evidence that the burden of health conditions has increased. Overall, reporting of longstanding illnesses has been stable for 30 years at around 30% of the population[15] and there is evidence that severity has actually lessened. Musculoskeletal conditions, circulatory diseases and mental health disorders account for over 70% of the burden of longstanding ill health.[16]

1.10   Some 15.4 million people in England have a longstanding illness,[17] and this is set to rise. Many of the diseases we now suffer from are linked to lifestyle and ageing. The numbers of people smoking, taking illicit drugs and drinking harmful levels of alcohol have all declined in recent years, but many of us still lead harmful lifestyles.

1.11   Wellbeing – a positive physical, social and mental state – is an important part of our health. Good wellbeing does not just mean the absence of mental illness – it brings a wide range of benefits, including reduced health risk behaviour (such as smoking), reduced mortality, improved educational outcomes and increased productivity at work. The data we have on wellbeing suggests that the UK is broadly on a par with France and Germany,[18] but there are likely to be wide variations within this across the country.

Wider factors influencing health, wellbeing and health inequalities

1.12   Our health and wellbeing is influenced by a wide range of factors – social, cultural, economic, psychological and environmental – across our lives. These change as we progress through the key transition points in life – from infancy and childhood, through our teenage years, to adulthood, working life, retirement and the end of life. Even before conception and through pregnancy, social, biological and genetic factors accumulate to influence the health of the baby.

Health inequalities – the evidence

Fair Society, Healthy Lives (2010),[19] the independent review of health inequalities in England commissioned by government and undertaken by Professor Sir Michael Marmot of University College London, sets out the implications of health inequalities. It makes it clear that material circumstance, social environment, psychosocial factors, behaviours and biological factors are all important influences on health. In practice, this means that in order to tackle health inequalities, we need to consider the much broader context of our lives. For instance, helping people into work can be very good for health. It provides not only income, but also – importantly – a stake in society. Early child development and educational attainment are also crucial for future health and wellbeing, as well as improving job opportunities and providing a route out of poverty.

While on the whole we are living longer than ever before, people's health and wellbeing varies significantly across England. And there is a social gradient of health – the lower a person's social position, the worse his or her health. People in disadvantaged areas are more likely to have shorter life expectancy and experience a greater burden of ill health – and there are differences in life expectancy and expectancy of life in good health across the socioeconomic spectrum. This inequality is driven by the underlying social factors that affect people's health and wellbeing – 'the causes of the causes'.

The Marmot Review states there are gaps of up to 7 years in life expectancy between the richest and poorest neighbourhoods, and up to 17 years in disability-free life expectancy (see Figure 1.2). It also highlights wide variation within areas; for instance in London, in one ward in Kensington and Chelsea, a man now has a life expectancy of 88 years, compared with 71 years in Tottenham Green, one of the capital's poorer wards. Low income and deprivation are particularly associated with higher levels of obesity, smoking, mental illness and harms arising from drug and alcohol misuse.

Protected equality characteristics can also have an impact on health. Evidence shows that inequalities based on race, disability, age, religion or belief, gender, sexual orientation and gender identity can interact in complex ways with socioeconomic position in shaping people's health. Some vulnerable groups and communities, for example people with learning disabilities or travellers, have significantly poorer life expectancy than would be expected based on their socioeconomic status alone.[20, 21]

1.13 We are all strongly influenced by the people around us, our families, the communities we live in and social norms. Our social and cognitive development, self-esteem, confidence, personal resilience and wellbeing are affected by a wide range of influences throughout life, such as the environment we live in, the place in which we work and our local community. This impacts on our health and our life chances.

Figure 1.2: Life expectancy and disability-free life expectancy at birth, by neighbourhood income level, England, 1999–2003

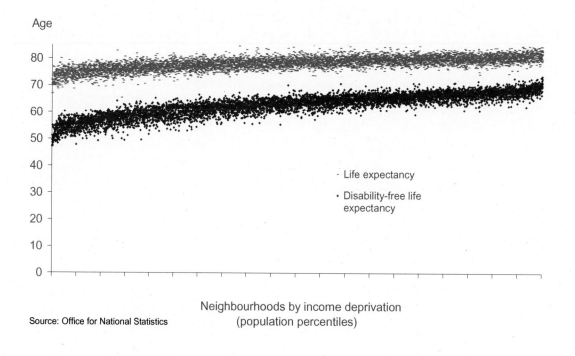

Source: Office for National Statistics

Neighbourhoods by income deprivation
(population percentiles)

> **Healthcare services have been estimated to contribute only a third of the improvements we could make in life expectancy – changing people's lifestyles and removing health inequalities contribute the remaining two thirds. Many of the biggest future threats to health, such as diabetes and obesity, are related to public health.[22]**

1.14 Figure 1.3 shows how location, take-up of healthcare services (in this case primary care) and deprivation play a role in outcomes for coronary heart disease sufferers in Birmingham – where there is a relationship between mortality and failure to register with a GP and thus receive treatment.

Figure 1.3: Variation in Birmingham – showing stark differences between the location of coronary heart disease patients registered with GPs (a), and the locations where coronary heart disease mortality rates are highest (b)

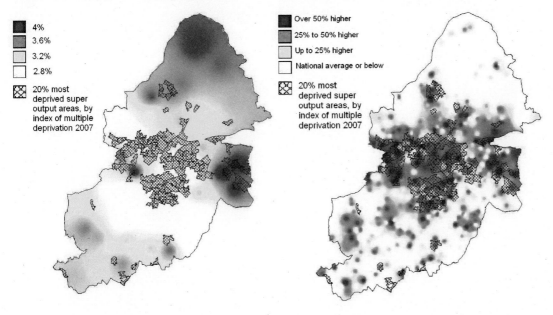

Figure 1.3a: Prevalence of coronary heart disease in Birmingham in 2008/09, according to GP Quality and Outcomes Framework data. Deprivation is also shown.

Figure 1.3b: Mortality from coronary heart disease in Birmingham in 2007-2009, according to data from the Office for National Statistics. Deprivation is also shown.

1.15 Recent research has shown that social networks exert a powerful influence on individual behaviour, affecting our weight, smoking habits and happiness.[23] Even people we do not know directly can affect our health and wellbeing.[24]

1.16 The quality of the environment around us also affects any community. Pollution, air quality, noise, the availability of green and open spaces, transport, housing, access to good-quality food and social isolation all influence the health and wellbeing of the local population. Climate change represents a challenge in terms of long-term health services planning and emergency preparedness.

Health and wellbeing challenges through life

Starting well

1.17 The health and wellbeing of women before, during and after pregnancy is a critical factor in giving children a healthy start in life and laying the groundwork for good health and wellbeing in later life.

1.18 Improving maternal mental health could lead to better outcomes in childhood. Maternal depression and anxiety in pregnancy and during a child's early life affects about 10–15% of pregnant women.[25] Rates are nearly twice as high among mothers living in poverty and three times as high for teenage mothers, and are associated with low birth weight, emotional or conduct disorders and children's later intellectual development.[26]

> **In one study, the children of women who were depressed at 3 months after giving birth had significantly lower IQ scores at 11 years. They also had problems with attention, had difficulties in mathematical reasoning, and were more likely than other children to have special educational needs.[27]**

1.19 There has been substantial progress in reducing infant deaths. In 2008, the infant mortality rate was the lowest ever recorded in England, with fewer than 5 deaths per 1,000 live births in England compared with 18 deaths per 1,000 live births in 1970.[28] However, these rates are higher than in comparable European countries and infant mortality is a key indicator of wider health inequalities. There is a 70% gap in infant mortality between the richest and poorest groups, and rates for some ethnic groups are almost twice the national average.[29]

1.20 There are opportunities to reduce infant mortality further by tackling maternal obesity (around 1 in 5 mothers could be overweight or obese);[30] increasing breastfeeding rates (England has one of the lowest rates in Europe and the current prevalence of breastfeeding at 6-8 weeks is 46.2%[31]) and decreasing smoking in pregnancy (more than 1 in 6 mothers smoke during pregnancy[32]). Smoking rates during pregnancy are much higher among lower socioeconomic groups[33] and teenage mothers.[34]

1.21 A total of 1 in 14 babies in the UK have a low birth weight (which is associated with immediate and longer-term health consequences for babies), a higher rate than the average for EU15 and EU27 countries.[35] This could also be improved by reducing smoking during pregnancy.[36]

1.22 Children's development is crucial for their future health and wellbeing and better early years support could make a big difference. Good parent–child relationships help build children's self-esteem and confidence and reduce the risk of children adopting unhealthy lifestyles. A total of 1 in 10 children are estimated to have emotional or behavioural problems,[37] which increase the risk of poor health and wellbeing both in childhood and later life.[38]

> **At birth, babies have around a quarter of the brain neurons of an adult. By the age of 3, the young child has around twice the number of neurons of an adult – making the early years critical for the development of the brain, language, social, emotional and motor skills.**

Developing well

1.23 There are opportunities to reduce road accidents – the leading cause of accidental death and injury of children in the UK, resulting in almost 21,000 injuries in 2009.[39] There are strong social and regional variations, so this lends itself to a tailored local approach.

1.24 Progress is being made in tackling childhood obesity – the rise among 2–10-year-olds from 1 in 10 children in 1995 to almost 1 in 7 in 2008 appears to be levelling off.[40] However, more than 1 in 5 children are still overweight or obese by age 3.[41] Rates are higher among some black and minority ethnic (BME) communities and in lower socioeconomic groups.[42]

> **Through social networks, obesity can actually be 'spread' by person-to-person interaction. Social norms affect other health areas too: if more than half of a student's social network smoke, then that student's risk of smoking doubles.[43]**

1.25 Teenagers and young people are among the biggest lifestyle risk-takers. About 1 in 5 young adults say they have recently used drugs, mostly cannabis.[44] Rates of STIs such as chlamydia are increasing, with 15–24-year-olds the most affected group. Around 1 in 10 of the people who get an STI will become re-infected within a year.[45] Teenage conceptions are at a 20-year low (40 cases per 1,000 under 18s), but are still high compared with Western Europe.[46]

1.26 Teenage years are a crucial time for health and wellbeing in later life. Half of lifetime mental illness (excluding dementia) starts by the age of 14.[47] More than 8 out of 10 adults who have ever smoked regularly started smoking before 19,[48] and one study found that 8 in 10 obese teenagers went on to be obese as adults.[49]

1.27 Around 1 in 3 young adults drink to the point of drunkenness, the highest rates among any age group.[50] Accidents due to alcohol (including drink-driving accidents) are the leading cause of death among 16–24 year-olds.[51]

Living well

1.28 Many premature deaths and illnesses could be avoided by improving lifestyles. It is estimated that a substantial proportion of cancers[52] and over 30% of deaths from circulatory disease[53] could be avoided, mainly through a combination of stopping smoking, improving diet and increasing physical activity.

1.29 Reducing smoking rates represents a huge opportunity for public health – smoking is the single biggest preventable cause of early death and illness. There are 2 million fewer smokers now than a decade ago, but 1 in 5 adults still smoke.[54] Smoking is estimated to cost the NHS at least £2.7 billion a year in England.[55]

1.30 2 out of 3 adults are overweight or obese.[56] The estimated cost to the NHS of obesity-related conditions is £4.2 billion each year, and diabetes is rising sharply.[57] Around 7 in 10 people consume more salt than is recommended[58] (leading to an estimated 1 in 3 people with high blood pressure[59]); only 3 in 10 adults eat the recommended 5 portions of fruit and vegetables a day;[60] and only 3 or 4 in 10 adults say they do the recommended levels of physical activity every week.[61]

1.31 The majority of the population either do not drink alcohol at all or, if they do drink, they do so within the Government's lower-risk limits.[62] However, regular heavy drinking is leading to a rapid rise in liver disease, which is now the fifth biggest cause of death in England. Drunkenness is associated with almost half of assaults and more than a quarter of domestic violence incidents.[63]

1.32 We have the lowest levels of illicit drug use since the British Crime Survey began measuring it in 1996. However, we have some of the highest levels of illicit drug use in Europe. More than 1 in 12 adults used an illicit drug in the last year.[64] As well as being exposed to health risks, drug users are more likely to be involved in crime (such as theft and prostitution), to be unemployed and to lose contact with friends and family.

1.33 Diagnoses of STIs are increasing. STIs can have serious consequences for health,[65] including infertility. More than 1 in 4 people with HIV are unaware that they are infected and around 1 in 2 new cases are diagnosed too late.[66]

1.34 Preventing mental ill health represents a huge opportunity: estimates of the burden of mental ill health range from 9%[67] to 23%[68] of the total health burden in the UK. The health and economic cost in England was estimated as £77.4 billion in 2003.[69] There is evidence that mental ill health disproportionately impacts on people from black and ethnic minority communities, the homeless and other socially excluded groups.[70]

1.35 People with mental ill health are much more likely to smoke and die younger, and a large number of people with mental health problems also have alcohol or drug problems. Over 1 in 3 people with a mental disorder smoke.[71]

> **One study found the life expectancy of people with schizophrenia was 15–20 years lower than that of the general population.[72]**

1.36 A total of 1 in 10 people are carers, and analysis of census data shows that 1 in 5 carers providing over 50 hours of care a week say they are in poor health, compared with 1 in 9 non-carers.[73]

1.37 Improving the environment in which people live can make healthy lifestyles easier. When the immediate environment is unattractive, it is difficult to make physical activity and contact with nature part of everyday life. Unsafe or hostile urban areas that lack green spaces and are dominated by traffic can discourage activity. Lower socioeconomic groups and those living in the more deprived areas experience the greatest environmental burdens.

Working well

1.38 The health and wellbeing of people of working age is critical to supporting the economy and society. Being in work is in general good for health, while being out of work can lead to poorer physical and mental health.[74]

1.39 Reducing working-age ill health has the potential to save the UK up to £100 billion a year, around the size of the entire annual NHS budget.[75] Around 172 million working days were lost to sickness absence in 2007, at a cost to the economy of over £13 billion.[76]

> Some 17% of people claiming incapacity benefit have a musculoskeletal condition, many of which are preventable.[77]

1.40 Taking a preventive approach to mental health presents a significant opportunity for reducing absence from work: 9.8 million working days were lost in Britain in 2009/10 due to work-related stress, depression or anxiety alone.[78]

Ageing well

1.41 Our population is ageing rapidly, but we are living longer and staying fitter for longer – today's 65-year-olds are more active and well than ever before.[79] Maintaining social networks, being part of a community and staying active all benefit health and wellbeing in later life. By 2024, an estimated 50% of the population will be over the age of 50, due to a combination of increased life expectancy and low birth rates. This is particularly significant in rural areas: the average age of rural residents is nearly six years older than people living in urban areas.[80]

1.42 Dementia affects around 750,000 people in the UK and numbers are expected to double by 2030.[81] The annual costs of dementia in the UK amount to £17 billion.[82] Half of dementias have a vascular component; by improving diet and lifestyle in earlier life we can significantly reduce their impact.

1.43 A total of 1 in 4 older people have symptoms of depression requiring professional intervention.[83] Better treatment for this group could improve their health outcomes considerably. Estimates suggest that around 1 in 10 older people experience chronic loneliness, with people living in deprived areas experiencing much higher rates.[84]

> Life expectancy at 65 is now more than 20 years for women, and more than 17 years for men – higher than it has ever been.[85]

1.44 There are increasing numbers of frail older people, and many people over 65 are also carers. In winter 2008/09, there were 35,000 excess deaths[86] in England, many of which could have been prevented.[87]

1.45 Each year 1 in 3 people over 65 and almost 1 in 2 people over 85 experience one or more falls, many of which are preventable.[88] Hip fracture is the most common serious injury related to falls in older people. Around 76,000 hip fractures occur in the UK each year,[89] costing the NHS £1.4 billion, and numbers may double by 2050.[90]

Seizing these opportunities

1.46 This White Paper sets out how society can seize these opportunities to improve the public's health and wellbeing and reduce health inequalities. The new system:

- will have a strategic focus on the outcomes that matter most;

- focus on doing what works in order to make the biggest difference;

- harness efforts across society – individuals, families, local and national government, and the private, voluntary and community sectors – to tackle these issues; and

- put local government in a leadership role as, given the huge variations across the country, local councils are best placed to address the particular issues that their areas face.

2. A radical new approach

Summary

The current approach and system is not up to the task of seizing these huge opportunities for better health and reduced inequalities in health. This White Paper sets out a radical new approach that will empower local communities, enable professional freedoms and unleash new ideas based on the evidence of what works, while ensuring that the country remains resilient to and mitigates against current and future health threats. This approach will reach across and reach out – addressing the root causes of poor health and wellbeing, reaching out to the individuals and families who need the most support – and be:

- **responsive** – owned by communities and shaped by their needs;

- **resourced** – with ring-fenced funding and incentives to improve;

- **rigorous** – professionally-led and focused on evidence; efficient and effective; and

- **resilient** – strengthening protection against current and future threats to health.

Protecting the population from health threats should be led by central government, with a strong system to the frontline. But beyond that, local leadership and wide responsibility across society is the way to improve everyone's health and wellbeing, and tackle the wider factors that influence it, most effectively. Efforts should be focused on the outcomes that matter most, doing what works best to get there, with transparency about outcomes to enable accountability. When central government needs to act, the approach will reflect the core values of freedom, fairness and responsibility by strengthening self-esteem, confidence and personal responsibility; positively promoting healthy behaviours and lifestyles; and adapting the environment to make healthy choices easier. We will balance the freedoms of individuals and organisations with the need to avoid harm to others, and we will use a 'ladder' of interventions to determine the least intrusive approach possible, aiming to make voluntary approaches work before resorting to regulation.

Reaching across and reaching out – addressing the root causes of ill health

2.1 There has not been enough focus on the root causes of ill health. Mental and physical health and wellbeing interact, and are affected by a wide range of influences throughout life.

2.2 Central government can play a part in shaping some of these influences and must have a firm grip both on protecting people against serious health threats and on preparing for emergencies. However, top-down initiatives and lectures from central government about the 'risks' are not the answer. And while the NHS will continue to have a critical role to play, it cannot tackle all the wider factors on its own.

2.3 A new approach is needed, which gets to the root causes of people's circumstances and behaviour, and integrates mental and physical health. The latest insights from behavioural science need to be harnessed to help enable and guide people's everyday decisions, particularly at the key transition points in their lives, such as when they start or leave school, start a family or retire.

2.4 Wider factors that shape the health and wellbeing of individuals, families and local communities – such as education, employment and the environment – also need to be addressed in order to tackle health inequalities.

2.5 Responsibility needs to be shared right across society – between individuals, families, communities, local government, business, the NHS, voluntary and community organisations, the wider public sector and central government:

- **Individuals should feel that they are in the driving seat for all aspects of their and their family's health, wellbeing and care.** This applies to people maintaining their wellbeing and preventing ill health; if they have a long-term condition, keeping as well as possible and managing it to avoid it worsening; and being true partners in their care so that decisions are shared as far as possible, based on the right information and genuine dialogue with health professionals. For public health as for social care, the vision is services and support delivered in a partnership between individuals, communities, the voluntary sector, the NHS and local government – including wider support services such as housing.

- **Local government is best placed to influence many of the wider factors that affect health and wellbeing.** We need to tap into this potential by significantly empowering local government to do more through real freedoms, dedicated resources and clear responsibilities, building on its existing important role in public health.

- **The NHS continues to have a crucial role.** Preventing ill health, screening for disease, supporting people with long-term conditions, improving access to care for the whole population and tackling health emergencies are all key functions that the NHS provides. GPs, community nurses, allied health professionals, dentists and pharmacists in the community, and hospital-based consultants and nurses all play a vital part.

- **Charities, voluntary organisations and community groups already make a vital contribution.** They provide services to individuals and communities, act as advocates for excluded groups and catalysts for action. The Government will encourage partnership working and opportunities for providers from all sectors to offer relevant services.

- **Businesses must take more responsibility for the impact of their practices on people's health and wellbeing.** The Government will work collaboratively with business and the voluntary sector through a new Responsibility Deal.

- **Employers from all sectors should look to support the health and wellbeing of their staff.** There are potentially major benefits for them and their staff if they do. The NHS will lead the way on this.

- **Central government will continue to play an important role.** We will directly co-ordinate activity to protect people from serious health threats and emergencies. And we will create the right system and incentives to free-up local communities to improve health and reduce inequalities, doing only what is necessary across central government to enable this. In all cases, we will ensure that we use proportionate and effective approaches, reflecting the core values of freedom, fairness and responsibility.

Responsive – owned by communities, shaped to meet their needs

2.6 Centralisation has failed. There have been far too many central initiatives, with power hoarded in Whitehall. Multiple top-down targets about improving health and reducing inequalities have been imposed on local communities.

2.7 We will end this top-down government. It is time to free up local government and local communities to decide how best to improve the health and wellbeing of their citizens, deciding what actions to take locally with the NHS and other key partners, without undue interference from the centre.

2.8   We propose to do this through new freedoms and funding for public health in local government. This will be supported by a proposed public health outcomes framework and a 'health premium', which will incentivise local government and communities to improve health and reduce inequalities, while leaving them free to decide how best to do this, in line with local needs. Data will be published to make it easier for local communities to compare themselves with others across the country and to incentivise improvements.

2.9   We have been working closely with partners, and will shortly consult on detailed proposals for a public health outcomes framework, so that local communities, local government, the NHS and other key partners have an opportunity to shape it. This will sit alongside the proposed NHS outcomes framework[91] and social care outcomes framework.[92] We propose that the public health outcomes framework should cover five broad 'domains' of public health:

- Domain 1 – Health protection and resilience: protecting people from major health emergencies and serious harm to health;

- Domain 2 – Tackling the wider determinants of ill health: addressing factors that affect health and wellbeing;

- Domain 3 – Health improvement: positively promoting the adoption of 'healthy' lifestyles;

- Domain 4 – Prevention of ill health: reducing the number of people living with preventable ill health; and

- Domain 5 – Healthy life expectancy and preventable mortality: preventing people from dying prematurely.

Resourced – based on ring-fenced funding, with incentives to improve

2.10   Public health budgets have been squeezed. Prevention has not enjoyed parity with NHS treatment, despite repeated attempts by central government to prioritise it. Public health funds have too often been raided at times of pressure in acute NHS services and short-term crises.

2.11   It is time to prioritise public health. The Government will ring-fence public health funds from within the overall NHS budget to ensure that it is prioritised, although it will still be subject to the running-cost reductions and efficiency gains that will be required across the system.

2.12 Alongside the shift of power from Whitehall to local communities we will allocate ring-fenced funds for public health to local authorities to enable them to secure better health and reduce inequalities, working with the NHS and other key partners in their areas.

Rigorous – professionally-led and focused on evidence; efficient and effective

2.13 The system has often let the workforce down. Public health professionals have been disempowered and their skills not sufficiently valued when compared with their counterparts in NHS acute services. We need to address the imbalance, so that prevention and public health enjoy true parity with treatment.

2.14 Subject to the passage of the Health and Social Care Bill, the Government proposes to set up a new public health service – Public Health England. This will be a uniting force for the wider family of professionals who also spend time on improving people's lives and tackling inequalities.

2.15 There is patchy use of evidence about 'what works'. Despite much activity at both national and local levels, further progress is needed to build and apply the evidence base for 'what works' and to ensure that resources are used most effectively and are linked to clear health outcomes. A culture of using the evidence to prioritise what we do and test out innovative ideas needs to be developed, while ensuring that new approaches are rigorously evaluated and that the learning is applied in practice.

2.16 The Government will harness the information revolution to make the best use of evidence and evaluation and support innovative approaches to behaviour change throughout society.

Resilient – strengthening protection against current and future threats to health

2.17 The current system for health protection is fragmented. The UK has responded excellently to public health incidents and emergencies in recent years, but the system lacks integration and is over-reliant on goodwill to make it work. A stronger, more integrated system is needed, which is equipped to meet future threats and has a clear line of sight from the top of government to the frontline.

2.18 The Government is therefore taking forward proposals for enhancing the functions of the Secretary of State for Health, making accountabilities in the system clearer and creating a new streamlined public health service to lead health protection and public health efforts across the country.

Intervening effectively

2.19 When central government needs to act, we will balance the freedoms of individuals and organisations with the need to avoid harm to others. We will aim to make voluntary approaches work before resorting to regulation.

2.20 The arguments about when it is appropriate for government to intervene in people's health and to what extent have become oversimplified. They are often presented as a straightforward choice between two extremes – intrusive intervention into people's lives or completely hands-off. These fail to capture the wide range of interventions that are available and the need to make decisions on a case-by-case basis about which to use.

2.21 A more sophisticated approach is needed. As Richard Reeves' independent report *A Liberal Dose?*[93] concluded, there is no 'magic equation' for how and when government should intervene. But there are some sensible criteria that government can apply, reflecting our core values.

2.22 **First, the Government will recognise that protecting and improving people's health covers a wide spectrum of issues that demand very different approaches.** The issues range from serious biological, chemical and infectious disease threats where central government must take a strong lead, to diseases such as diabetes, heart disease and depression, which are linked to people's lifestyles and situations and require local solutions that are tailored to people's different needs.

2.23 **Second, the Government will balance the freedoms of individuals and organisations with the need to avoid serious harm to others.** We will look carefully at the strength of the case before deciding to intervene and to what extent. This must be based on a rigorous assessment of the evidence about health and wider harms, with the potential benefits balanced against the social and economic costs to individuals, organisations and wider society.

2.24 **Third, the Government will consider different approaches for different groups of the population, taking account of the significant barriers that some people face.** We will treat capable, responsible and informed adults as adults. We will treat children differently as they rely more on adults to help make decisions or to make decisions for them when they are very young. We should also recognise that some individuals may need more support because they face particular barriers. We need to use different approaches for different people, drawing on the latest evidence from behavioural science to do this.

A 'ladder' of interventions

2.25 The public expect government to prepare for and tackle serious, unavoidable threats and emergencies – such as radiation, chemical spills, pandemic flu or terrorism – on their behalf. These cases can demand direct intervention from a range of central government departments and need the firm grip of the Secretary of State for Health.

2.26 There are also some activities that it makes sense to do once at national level rather than repeat many times over at local level. This includes making sure that air, food and water meet safety standards; buying vaccines and planning immunisation programmes; providing specialist expertise to support local incidents; and legislating to ban some types of drugs.

2.27 Across all these areas, government needs to keep up its guard, ensuring that it is vigilant against existing and emerging health threats and is fully prepared to respond if and when they arise.

2.28 When it comes to improving people's health and wellbeing, we need a different approach. We cannot just ban everything, lecture people or deliver initiatives to the public. This is not justified and will not work. Nor should we have one-size-fits-all policies that often leave the poorest in our society to struggle.

2.29 Few of us consciously choose 'good' or 'bad' health. We all make personal choices about how we live and behave: what to eat, what to drink and how active to be. We all make trade-offs between feeling good now and the potential impact of this on our longer-term health. In many cases, moderation is often the key.

2.30 All capable adults are responsible for these very personal choices. At the same time, we do not have total control over our lives or the circumstances in which we live. A wide range of factors constrain and influence what we do, both positively and negatively.

2.31 The Government's approach to improving health and wellbeing – relevant to both national and potential local actions – is therefore based on the following actions, which reflect the Coalition's core values of freedom, fairness and responsibility. These are:

- strengthening self-esteem, confidence and personal responsibility;

- positively promoting 'healthier' behaviours and lifestyles; and

- adapting the environment to make healthy choices easier.

2.32 The Nuffield Council on Bioethics' 'intervention ladder' shows the range of potential approaches which could be used to promote positive lifestyle changes in this way (see Figure 2.1).[94] The options range from the least intrusive into people's lives (such as just providing information) to the most intrusive (eliminating people's choice about what they do through legislation):

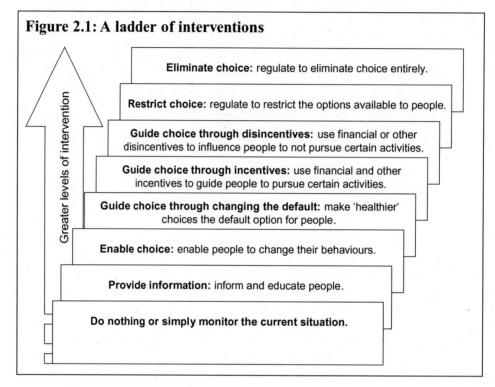

Figure 2.1: A ladder of interventions

Greater levels of intervention →

Eliminate choice: regulate to eliminate choice entirely.

Restrict choice: regulate to restrict the options available to people.

Guide choice through disincentives: use financial or other disincentives to influence people to not pursue certain activities.

Guide choice through incentives: use financial and other incentives to guide people to pursue certain activities.

Guide choice through changing the default: make 'healthier' choices the default option for people.

Enable choice: enable people to change their behaviours.

Provide information: inform and educate people.

Do nothing or simply monitor the current situation.

2.33 Where the case for central action is justified, the Government will aim to use the least intrusive approach necessary to achieve the desired effect. We will in particular seek to use approaches that focus on enabling and guiding people's choices wherever possible.

2.34 This includes changing social norms and default options so that healthier choices are easier for people to make. There is significant scope to use approaches that harness the latest techniques of behavioural science to do this – nudging people in the right direction rather than banning or significantly restricting their choices.

2.35 Working through our new Public Health Responsibility Deal, the Government will aim to base these approaches on voluntary agreements with business and other partners, rather than resorting to regulation or top-down lectures. However, if these partnership approaches fail to work, the Government will consider the case for 'moving up' the intervention ladder where necessary. For example, if voluntary commitments from business are not met after an agreed time period, we will consider the case for introducing change through regulation in the interests of people's health.

3. Health and wellbeing throughout life

Summary

The Government is radically shifting power to local communities, enabling them to improve health throughout people's lives, reduce inequalities and focus on the needs of the local population. This chapter highlights local innovation and outlines the cross-government framework that will enable local communities to reduce inequalities and improve health at key stages in people's lives, including:

a. **empowering local government and communities, who will have new resources, rights and powers to shape their environments and tackle local problems;**

b. **taking a coherent approach to different stages of life and key transitions, instead of tackling individual risk factors in isolation.** Mental health will be a key element, and we will shortly publish a new mental health strategy;

c. **giving every child in every community the best start in life.** We will support this through our continued commitment to reduce child poverty, by investing to increase health visitor numbers, doubling by 2015 the number of families reached through the Family Nurse Partnership (FNP) programme, and refocusing Sure Start Children's Centres for those who need them most. An Olympic and Paralympic-style sports competition will be offered to all schools from 2012;

d. **making it pay to work,** through comprehensive welfare reforms, creating new jobs through local growth and working with employers to unleash their potential as champions of public health;

e. **designing communities for active ageing and sustainability.** We will make active ageing the norm rather than the exception, for example by building more Lifetime Homes, protecting green spaces and launching physical activity initiatives, including a £135 million Lottery investment in a Mass Participation and Community Sport legacy programme and a volunteer led walks programme. We will protect and promote community ownership of green spaces and improve access to land so that people can grow their own food; and

f. **working collaboratively with business and the voluntary sector through the Public Health Responsibility Deal** with five networks on food, alcohol, physical activity, health at work and behaviour change. We plan to launch the Deal in early 2011 and expect to be able to announce agreements on further reformulation of food to reduce salt; better information for consumers about food; and promotion of more socially responsible retailing and consumption of alcohol. It will also develop the Change4Life campaign, for example through the 'Great Swapathon', £250 million of partner-funded vouchers to make healthy lifestyle choices easier.

A partnership approach through life

3.1 This White Paper is the Government's response to *Fair Society, Healthy Lives* – the Marmot Review.[95] It adopts an approach which addresses the wider factors that affect people at different stages and key transition points in their lives, and reflects the review's principle of 'proportionate universalism' – by which the scale and intensity of action is proportionate to the level of disadvantage.

3.2 The Government wants all parts of society taking responsibility for health and wellbeing. This White Paper supports the shift to make that happen across government, outlining the high-level framework to empower local communities to deliver local change, and highlighting the opportunities for local government, the private and voluntary sectors to play their part.

3.3 This change will only happen if we base our approach on the reality of people's lives, rather than on policy areas considered in isolation. Consequently, this chapter is framed around those key points and stages in people's lives when mental and physical health outcomes can be most strongly influenced.

3.4 We expect most action to happen at a local level: helping people improve their mental and physical health, wellbeing and resilience, and tailoring support to the different needs of individuals and families at different stages in their lives. By giving local government control of public health resources, we will shift power and accountability to local communities and create healthy places to grow up and grow older in, with new partnerships in important areas, such as housing, planning, schools and transport. As set out in the previous chapter, the role of central government will be to establish a framework so that local action can be most effective, and to do nationally only the things that need to be done at that level. This includes working across multiple departments to address the wider determinants of health through the new Cabinet Sub-Committee on Public Health. This chapter sets out the range of actions we will take across central government.

Starting well

3.5 Starting well, through early intervention and prevention, is a key priority for the Government, developing strong universal public health and early education with an increased focus on disadvantaged families. This approach, proportionate universalism, was advocated in the Marmot Review into health inequalities.

3.6 In local government, there will be new opportunities to develop integrated local strategies between public health services, children's services and the NHS, aligning outcomes and resources. At neighbourhood level, increased numbers of health visitors, working with children's centres and GPs, will lead and deliver the Healthy Child programme, alongside the evidence-based Family Nurse Partnership (FNP) programme. These services, working with partners, will support families to build community capacity as part of the Big Society. Supporting parents with parenting programmes has a positive impact on both parents' and children's wellbeing and mental health. The Healthy Child Programme also includes breastfeeding support and a range of proven preventive services.

3.7 High-quality universal services will form the foundations to ensure the strongest outcomes for children and their parents. The Department of Health will work with the NHS to continue to strengthen the preventive aspects of maternity services. The Department for Education will continue to offer all families 15 hours a week of high-quality free nursery care for preschool children. The Healthy Child Programme will continue to be delivered by increased numbers of health visitors and their teams, the primary care team, midwives and early years workers, all providing support to families.

3.8 The Department of Health will increase investment in health visitors, through a four-year transformational programme, and will publish a plan shortly. Health visitors will have a new role in building a stronger local community, in partnership with local voluntary and community groups, peer support and befriending networks. The proposed health and wellbeing board and the Joint Strategic Needs Assessment will be key mechanisms to enable high-quality public health input into the commissioning of health visiting services and to strengthen the critical links with other services such as early years services, including children's centres, maternity services and primary care.

3.9 We will also do more to improve the outcomes of those families in need of more intensive support by doubling the capacity of the FNP programme and supporting health visitors to work with families needing additional early intervention. The first phase of single Community Budgets for families with complex needs will enable a focus on prevention through locally co-ordinated support for families with multiple problems.

3.10 Children's centres locally will focus particularly on engaging with families where children are at risk of poor outcomes to ensure that they are ready to thrive when they start school. They will act as hubs for family support and as a base for voluntary and community groups. They will also be alert to children who may be being harmed and take the necessary action to protect them.

3.11 Central government will continue to tackle child poverty, aiming to eradicate it by 2020, and will publish a strategy for child poverty in the spring. We are also committed to investigating a new approach to supporting vulnerable families, potentially through intensive intervention models such as Family Intervention Projects and group parenting programmes.

3.12 Wider society, including employers, has a role to play in supporting families. The Department of Health will work in partnership with employers to encourage breastfeeding-friendly employment policies, through pilots involving an acute NHS trust, over 300 children's centres in areas with low breastfeeding rates, a primary school and a secondary school.

Developing well

3.13 The shift of power from central government to schools and local communities provides new opportunities and incentives to forge local partnerships to deliver better health outcomes for children and young people. The pupil and health premiums will ensure that funding is weighted to address inequalities and narrow the gap in health and education.

3.14 We expect excellent health and pastoral support to continue to be a hallmark of good schools. Good schools understand well the connections between pupils' physical and mental health, their safety, and their educational attainment. However, it is not for government to tell schools how they should do this. Schools will be able to draw on additional expertise from local health professionals and children's services, to best meet the needs of their pupils.

3.15 Directors of Public Health (DsPH) will be able to work with their local authority children's services colleagues, schools and other partners to determine local strategies for improving child health and wellbeing. They will be supported by consolidation of existing guidance into best practice resources for schools, further education and training providers. The Healthy Schools, Healthy Further Education and Healthy Universities programmes will continue to be developed by their respective sectors, as voluntary programmes, collaborating where appropriate and exploring partnership working with business and voluntary bodies.

3.16 Good schools will be active promoters of health in childhood and adolescence, because healthy children with high self-esteem learn and behave better at school. Within the current non-statutory personal, social and health education (PSHE) framework, schools will provide age-appropriate teaching on relationships and sexual health, substance misuse, diet, physical activity and some mental health issues. The Department for Education (DfE) will conduct an internal review to determine how they can support schools to improve the quality of all PSHE teaching, including giving teachers the flexibility to use their judgement about how best to deliver PSHE education. Schools will also have a role in tackling these issues as part of their pastoral role, linking to local agencies and community groups where appropriate. Central government will also bring together a group of experts to identify non-legislative solutions to tackling low levels of body confidence and will take account of their views when developing policy.

3.17 As young people move through their teenage years and make the transition into adulthood, our aim is to strengthen their ability to take control of their lives, within clear boundaries, and help reduce their susceptibility to harmful influences, in areas such as sexual health, teenage pregnancy, drugs and alcohol. And they should have easy access to health services they trust, for example accredited 'You're Welcome' young-people-friendly services. Public health funding, alongside the new early intervention grant, will allow local areas to develop a tailored approach that responds to the needs, age and vulnerability of the young person, and particularly targets at-risk groups.

3.18 Improving self-esteem and developing positive social norms throughout the school years should be the focus of local strategies and will be supported by information about effective behavioural interventions for self-esteem. We need to develop approaches that tackle the root causes of failure, rather than reacting to behavioural problems with programmes designed to tackle their symptoms. School-based mental health promotion can improve self-esteem and reduce risky behaviour, particularly for those at higher risk.

3.19 Families will be supported to make informed choices about their diet and their levels of physical activity, including through updated guidelines on physical activity. The Department of Health will broaden the Change4Life programme to take a more holistic approach to childhood issues, for instance covering mental wellbeing and strategies to help parents talk to their children about other health issues and behaviour, such as alcohol. The Department for Education will maintain existing standards for school food.

3.20 Children need access to high-quality physical education (PE), so DfE will ensure the requirement to provide PE in all maintained schools is retained and will provide new support to encourage a much wider take up of competitive team sports. The Department for Culture, Media and Sport (DCMS) will create an Olympic and Paralympic-style school sports competition, which will be offered to all schools from 2012, building on Change4Life clubs in schools. This year the Government is supporting walking and cycling in schools through the Department of Health's Living Streets 'Walk Once A Week' initiative and the Department of Transport's (DfT) funding for Bikeability cycle training. We are working towards every child being offered high-quality instruction on how to ride safely and confidently by the end of year 6 of school.

3.21 The Healthy Child Programme for school-age children will continue to be commissioned to provide those developing services with a clinical evidence based framework, including an expanded talking therapies service. The National Child Measurement Programme will continue to run, providing local areas with information about levels of overweight and obesity in children to inform planning and commissioning of local services.

3.22 Responding to local need, the school nursing service will work with other professionals to support schools in developing health reviews at school entry and key transitions, managing pupils' wellbeing, medical and long-term condition needs and developing schools as health-promoting environments. The Department of Health is developing a new vision for school nurses, reflecting their broad public health role in the school community.

London vs New York schools walking competition

Technological advances and behavioural insights are blended together in this innovative approach to encouraging exercise in children. Pupils at two secondary schools in London were offered incentives to walk to school through Step2Get, using new near field communication (NFC) technology. In a partnership between Intelligent Health and Transport for London (TfL), each student was provided with a swipe card which they touched on receivers placed on lampposts along a safe walking route to school.

Each completed walk to school was converted to points and these were redeemed as rewards as part of an online game. There was a resulting 18% shift to walking. For every £1 invested in Step2Get, there was a £24 benefit to TfL and the local authority, linked to a reduction of 48% in police time due to less overcrowding at bus stops and on buses and fewer accidents.

In 2011/12, secondary schools in London will compete against those in New York using the same NCF technology. An estimated 30,000 students will take part, with each school competing to accumulate the greatest number of completed walks along the safe routes to school. The overall winning city will be announced at the time of the 2012 London Olympic and Paralympic Games.

There is a strong theme of behavioural science underlying this initiative. Reframing the concept of exercise as a fun and positive game taps into salience, while rewards and the social aspect strongly incentivise a change in behaviour.

As part of the London 2012 legacy, the technology will be available as a social enterprise to any school in the world. This will encourage thousands of children worldwide to walk safely and be more active, and will reduce carbon dioxide emissions associated with travel.

www.intelligenthealth.co.uk/services/schools.html

3.23 For children and adolescents with mental health problems, central government will support interventions that promote mental health resilience and effective early treatment, including talking therapies, thus reducing the likelihood of problems extending into adulthood. The Department of Health will shortly set out its approach in a mental health strategy. We will continue to tackle violence and abuse that can damage the physical and mental health of children, either through direct experience or witnessing violence in their household. Child protection services will also be able to work more closely with public health within local government. Safeguarding duties will of course continue to apply to health services commissioned under the new arrangements for local government.

3.24 Central and local government are responsible for protecting children through tobacco control legislation and enforcement, including preventing sales to under-18-year-olds.

3.25 Since the prohibition of tobacco advertising, the only way that tobacco products can be promoted is at the point of sale. The Government will look at whether the plain packaging of tobacco products could be an effective way to reduce the number of young people taking up smoking and to help those who are trying to quit smoking. The Government wants to make it easier for people to make healthy choices, but will clearly need to make sure that there is good evidence to demonstrate that plain packaging would have a public health benefit, as well as carefully exploring the competition, trade and legal implications of the policy. Details on how we propose to proceed will be set out in the Tobacco Control Plan.

3.26 The recent legislation to stop tobacco sales from vending machines will come into effect on 1 October 2011, so removing an easy source of cigarettes from under-age smokers and a source of temptation for adults trying to quit. We are also considering options for the display of tobacco in shops, recognising the need to take action both to reduce tobacco consumption and to reduce burdens on businesses. An announcement about this will follow shortly.

3.27 Adolescence is a significant transition point for young people, particularly young disabled people, those with special educational needs and those not in education, employment or training. The forthcoming Special Educational Needs and Disability Green Paper will set out in detail the Government's plans to improve outcomes for children and young people, to promote greater choice for their families across health, education, social care and other services, and to support transitions.

3.28 To support the transition from school to further education or work, the Government has pledged to create up to 75,000 additional apprenticeship places by 2014/15. We are committed to the participation of all 16 and 17-year-olds in education or training and to raising the participation age to 18 by 2015. We will ensure that young people have access to independent, high-quality careers advice – supporting young people not in training or education to get a good start to their working life. We will improve self-esteem, and promote personal responsibility and a more engaged and cohesive society through National Citizen Service, which we will pilot for around 10,000 young people in summer 2011.

Living well

3.29 For a long time, central government's default position has been to solve problems by drawing more power to the centre and lecturing people about how to live well. This often does not work. Therefore, we are turning to local communities to devise local solutions which work for them, to create the right kind of environment and build a critical mass of opinion to change behaviours.

3.30 Rather than central government nagging individuals and businesses to become more healthy, we believe that sustained behaviour change will only come about with a new approach – genuine partnership. A key component of our approach is the Public Health Responsibility Deal. We are working collaboratively with business and the voluntary sector, and have established five networks on food, alcohol, physical activity, health at work and behaviour change. We plan to launch the Deal in early 2011 and expect to be able to announce agreements on further reformulation of food to reduce salt; better information for consumers about food; and promotion of more socially responsible retailing and consumption of alcohol. And during January 2011's Change4Life 'Great Swapathon', partners will give £250 million of vouchers to make healthy lifestyle choices easier.

Change4Life Convenience Store Programme

This partnership between the Department of Health and the Association of Convenience Stores is aimed at increasing the availability and sales of fresh fruit and vegetables in convenience stores in deprived areas. Work includes the positioning of dedicated fruit and vegetable chiller cabinets in prominent positions and the use of Change4Life branding.

By March 2010, 160 stores in four regions were retailing fresh fruit and vegetables using the popular Change4Life brand. By March 2011, Change4Life convenience stores will be active in every region of the country. Evaluation shows an increase in sales of fruit and vegetables of up to 50% in some stores. Participating stores have also seen total sales rising across the board by an average of 11%, and the percentage of customers saying the store was a good place to shop overall rising from 43% to 54%.

Many stores have used the programme to engage with local schools and cooking clubs and are supporting them through fruit tuck shops, providing fruit at parents' evenings and providing fresh ingredients for use in cooking lessons at cost price.

3.31 The Department for Environment, Food and Rural Affairs' (Defra) Fruit and Vegetable Task Force has recommended that food containing fruit or vegetables with other types of food should be added to the 5 A DAY licensing scheme. This work is ongoing with industry and the voluntary sector. In addition, Government Buying Standards for food will support more balanced choices in areas that central government is directly responsible for, such as in its own workplaces.

3.32 Active travel and physical activity need to become the norm in communities. The Department of Health will support local areas by providing good evidence on how to make regular physical activity and healthy food choices easier for their populations, for example by sharing learning from the experiences of the nine 'Healthy Towns', as well as sustainable travel and cycle towns. Initial evidence from the first round of cycle towns showed that there was an increase in cycling across all social groups combined with a reduction in sedentary behaviour and single car use, when compared with people in similar towns.

3.33 Local sustainable transport, including active travel, will be supported through the Department for Transport's £560 million Local Sustainable Transport Fund. We will also be outlining how we will further support local authorities to take forward sustainable transport in the upcoming Local Transport White Paper.

Health inequalities, sustainability and climate change

'The sustainability agenda and climate change can help frame the way healthy communities and places are created… and create conditions that enable everyone to flourish equally.'[96]

The cognitive bias of most people means that they are likely to discount the future for the sake of the present and are more likely to respond to instant rewards.[97] The Marmot Review argues that climate change is one of the biggest public health threats of the 21st century,[98] with the potential to increase health inequalities. There are community responses that can help address long-term challenges like climate change while having a positive impact on health in the short-term, through:

- active travel – delivering low-cost health improvements and reducing emissions;

- green spaces – improving mental health and the quality of community life, offering some protection from the expected increase in heatwaves and flooding;

- spatial planning – promoting local ownership and occupation of public spaces;

- behaviour change – embedding new ways of sustainable living and working; and

- community projects to harness renewable energy – mitigating the effects of climate change.

3.34 Building on the Olympics, DCMS has announced a £100 million Mass Participation and Community Sport legacy programme, which will improve community sport facilities, improve and protect playing fields for community use, provide opportunities for sports volunteers and leaders, and deliver an open programme of personal challenge. The Walking for Health programme of volunteer-led health walks and Let's Get Moving will also provide important opportunities for people to be active.

3.35 Local government and communities will have new resources, rights and powers to shape their local areas. The Department for Communities and Local Government (DCLG) will support local areas with streamlined planning policy that aligns social, economic, environmental and health priorities into one place. Health considerations are an important part of planning policy and DCLG will consider how to take this forward in the new National Planning Policy Framework.

3.36 Access to green spaces is associated with better mental and physical health across socioeconomic groups. DCLG is working with Defra to create a new designation to protect green areas of particular importance to local communities and providing practical guidance to support community groups in the ownership of public spaces. It is intended that, through this new designation, people will have improved access to land, enabling them to grow their own food.

3.37 Defra will also lead a national campaign to increase tree-planting throughout England, particularly in areas where increased tree cover would help to improve residents' quality of life and reduce the negative effects of deprivation, including health inequalities. The charity Campaign for Greener Healthcare has developed a five-year project to improve the health of staff and patients through access to green spaces. It aims to plant one tree per employee – over a million trees – on NHS land. As well as green spaces, good air quality and reducing noise pollution are important issues for public health and wellbeing. Defra will publish information about local air quality and noise levels, empowering local government and communities to take action.[99] Finally, there is growing interest in promoting access to so called 'blue spaces' such as inland waterways and 'yellow spaces' (beaches and coastlines).

Run Dem Crew and the Nike 'Grid'

Three years ago, Charlie Dark, a teacher, writer and DJ in Hackney, east London, came up with a novel idea to empower local young people. He created a running club called Run Dem Crew (RDC), partnering with sportswear company Nike. RDC is based at Nike's 1948 Brand Space in Shoreditch and combines running and creative arts workshops to turn regular running into a trendy social activity.

Teaming up with the charities Fairbridge and the Active Communities Network, the concept has spread throughout England: 11 crews now exist in five different cities across the UK, led by 25 volunteer champions. In October 2010, all crews took part in a competitive event linked to the 'Grid', Nike's real-time online running-based gaming and social network. Crew members were encouraged to 'own the Grid' – to reclaim the streets as a safe and exhilarating place in which to live and play.

This innovative idea builds on lessons from behavioural science and aims to turn a generation of gamers into runners. Charlie Dark inspires young people, and uses creative workshops as a 'hook' to get young people interested in running. The social aspect of the running crews changes the perceived norm among young people that running is a boring, solitary activity. Running clubs have to earn the right to call themselves a RDC, and the support from Nike that that entails.

www.rundemcrew.com

3.38 The introduction of the Licensing Act 2003 and 24-hour licences promised to introduce a continental-style café culture. Instead, in 2009/10 nearly half of all violent crime was alcohol-related and communities are fighting a constant and expensive battle against alcohol-related crime and anti-social behaviour. The Home Office will seek to overhaul the Licensing Act to give local authorities and police stronger powers to remove licences from, or refuse licences to, any clubs, bars and pubs that are causing problems, close any shop or bar found to be persistently selling alcohol to children and charge more for late-night licences. The Home Office is committed to implementing the ban on selling alcohol below cost without delay.

Healthy Living Pharmacies, Portsmouth

Healthy Living Pharmacies (HLPs) are making a real difference to the health of people in Portsmouth, with 10 pharmacies awarded HLP status by NHS Portsmouth. HLPs have to demonstrate consistent, high-quality delivery of a range of services such as stopping smoking, weight management, emergency hormonal contraception, chlamydia screening, advice on alcohol and reviews of the use of their medicines. They proactively promote a healthy living ethos and work closely with local GPs and other health and social care professionals.

Early indications show that HLPs have greater productivity and offer higher-quality services. Early evaluation results include a 140% increase in smoking quits from pharmacies compared with the previous year; and 75% of the 200 smokers with asthma or chronic obstructive pulmonary disease who had a medicines use review accepted help to stop smoking.

www.portsmouth.nhs.uk/Services/Guide-to-services/resources-for-professionals.htm

3.39 Reducing smoking will continue to be a focus for public health. We will work to create environments that further discourage smoking and help bring about cultural change to make it less attractive. The Department of Health will publish the Tobacco Control Plan shortly. We will maintain the current smokefree laws in England. We will publish an academic review of the evidence about the impact of the legislation alongside the Tobacco Control Plan, showing high levels of compliance and public support. By creating the right environment for more people to take responsibility for their health, individuals benefit and there is also less cost to the taxpayer.

3.40 NHS Health Checks will continue to be offered to men and women aged 40 to 74. Everyone receiving an NHS Health Check will receive individually tailored advice and support to help manage their risk of heart disease, stroke and diabetes. The assessment can be carried out in a variety of settings, including pharmacy and community settings and the workplace, to help ensure that the service is accessible to all those eligible, including those in groups at highest risk of these diseases. The Department of Health will strengthen its partnership working with the pharmaceutical industry and community pharmacies to secure their support and investment in campaigns to promote effective routes to quit smoking.

3.41 The Department of Health will align funding streams on drug and alcohol treatment services across the community and in criminal justice settings. Funding will incentivise recovery outcomes while maintaining key public health measures such as needle exchange schemes. It is critical that, where appropriate, people are diverted from the criminal justice system to health services. There they can receive treatment for mental illness and drug and alcohol misuse, with benefits to their health and reducing their risk of reoffending.

3.42 Public health professionals will work locally to prevent people from taking harmful drugs, to reduce the drug use of those already taking drugs, and to help people to be drug free, recover fully and contribute to society. Details of our approach will be set out in a forthcoming cross-government drugs strategy. It will seek to prevent people taking illicit drugs at all ages, and arrest the slide into dependency.

Altogether Better Community Health Champions

Altogether Better started out as a BIG Lottery-funded regional collaborative and has grown to become a movement with a network that reaches beyond its original Yorkshire and the Humber region to as far away as China. Altogether Better aims to build capacity to empower individuals and communities to improve their own health and wellbeing through a flexible, locally tailored Community Health Champions approach.

Individuals from communities with high health risks are recruited and receive training and support to build their knowledge, confidence and social networks. These skills are used to carry out philanthropic activities so that the Champions act as a positive influence on peers within their homes, their workplace and the community. They are then supported to follow pathways of civic participation, education, employment and enterprise. In only three years there are already over 12,000 Community and Workplace Health Champions who have reached an estimated 60,000 others.

As a key aspect of this work, Altogether Better has built a sound practical evidence base for this approach. This evidence shows that the approach is improving health, as well as increasing individual and community social capital, voluntary activities and wider civic participation. Movement along pathways to education, paid employment and enterprise is also enhanced.

www.altogetherbetter.org.uk

3.43 We will work towards an integrated model of service delivery to allow easy access to confidential, non-judgemental sexual health services (including for sexually transmitted infections, contraception, abortion, health promotion and prevention). The Department of Health is piloting interventions on alcohol misuse linked to sexual health risks in order to manage broader risk-taking behaviour. We will also publish the results of an evidence review for sexual health which will help develop targeted interventions for particular groups, taking account of their specific needs and motivations.

3.44 Central government will sequence social marketing for public health through the life course so that, at each stage in a person's life, there is a meaningful and trusted voice. We will also scale back the number of brands that we support. We will trial new ways of changing behaviours, using emerging ideas from behavioural science, such as the use of social norms, changing defaults and providing incentives. We will publish a social marketing strategy, setting out our plans in more detail, in spring 2011.

The Lesbian and Gay Foundation: Face2Face counselling service, Manchester

Face2Face (F2F) was established in 2008 to provide lesbian and gay people in Manchester with a local service sensitive to the needs of the community. In February 2008, the service implemented the CORE (clinical outcomes routine evaluation) system, which provides a widely recognised quality evaluation of psychological therapies through the monitoring of key outcomes. Since then, over 300 clients have accessed the counselling service reporting a 53% reduction in the average pre-therapy score, taking the client from moderate to low levels of distress. CORE also allows demographic monitoring, to ensure that the service is reaching marginalised groups within the community.

www.lgf.org.uk

3.45 Working with other agencies, public health services will also have a role in tackling violence and abuse. In line with the recently published cross-government strategy, *Call to end violence against women and girls*,[100] the Department of Health produced *Improving services for women and child victims of violence*,[101] setting out how we will improve the health response to violence, building on the findings and recommendations of an independent taskforce. This includes work to improve access to and the quality of sexual assault referral centres (SARCs), which provide medical examinations, treatments and access to long-term support and counselling. We are taking forward the Government's commitment on sharing non-confidential data on gun and knife crime between hospitals and the police.

Working well

3.46 The Government is creating the right framework for enterprise and job creation. Enabling more people to work, safeguarding and improving their health at work, and supporting disabled people or people who have health conditions to enter, stay in or return to work are critical components of our public health challenge. Central and local government will support economic growth, make it pay to work through radical reform of the welfare system and provide support to people trying to enter work. For those in work, government will work in partnership with business to safeguard and improve health at work, and support disabled people, people with health conditions or people with caring responsibilities to stay in or return to work.

3.47 Local government, central government and businesses are working to create new jobs and opportunities. We will work in partnership, creating strong, sustainable growth, creating access to opportunities for all, supported by the £1.4 billion Regional Growth Fund over three years. Central government is supporting the creation of apprenticeships, internships, work pairing and college and workplace training places, creating opportunities for development for the most disadvantaged, including disabled people. We will also promote the expansion of volunteering opportunities that can be an effective route to gaining skills and employment, for example by supporting the training of volunteer Community Learning Champions to engage local people in learning activities, acquiring new skills and embarking on new career routes.

3.48 Central government is making it pay to work. A reformed Welfare to Work programme is being developed, ensuring that work always pays by replacing existing means-tested working-age benefits with a single Universal Credit. Existing support will be consolidated into a new integrated Work Programme to provide support for people to move into work; Work Choice will provide support for severely disabled people entering work; and existing adult careers advice has been simplified into a single service called NextStep.

3.49 Central government is also helping people to stay in work. Our innovative Fit for Work Service pilots are multi-disciplinary projects delivered by local providers, focusing on early intervention and designed to get workers who are off sick back to work faster and to keep them in work. The programme is being evaluated and the results, due in late 2011, will enable us to determine what works and in what circumstances.

3.50 The new Fit Note was introduced in April 2010, allowing GPs and individuals to focus on how to get people on sick leave back into work. Central government will support the NHS to embed this and implement the Fit Note electronically in GP surgeries as soon as possible. We are also examining the incentives in the sickness absence system, with a view to reducing the numbers of people who fall out of work due to health conditions and end up on benefits.

3.51 New provisions in the Equality Act 2010 came into force on 1 October. The Act prohibits employers from asking health or health-related questions before offering employment, except where it is an intrinsic function of the job. There is little evidence that pre-employment health screening identifies fitness for work. This empowers occupational health professionals to divert resources away from pre-employment health screening to preventive initiatives for all staff in the workplace.

3.52 Central government, in conjunction with the Faculty of Occupational Medicine, is developing an accreditation process for the new occupational health service standards. All employers will be encouraged to contract only those services that are fully accredited, and to seek preventive interventions. We are exploring a range of models which will help support small and medium-sized enterprises in promoting the health of their workforce, drawing on the expertise of larger companies, the NHS and the broader community, and promoting the better management of chronic conditions in the workplace.

3.53 The Department of Health will work in partnership with employers, through the Public Health Responsibility Deal, to improve health at work. Employers have the opportunity to improve health outcomes in areas from obesity to smoking, substance misuse and physical activity in their employees, employees' families and wider local communities. They can achieve this through establishing a strong cultural lead, strengthening management training in recognising and responding to the health needs of the workforce, and working more closely with others, particularly occupational health and primary care.

3.54 Central government will provide the evidence and data needed to raise awareness among employers of the clear case for investing in the health of their employees. This includes further development of the Change4Life employee wellness programme and the promotion of the Workplace Wellbeing Tool to help organisations assess progress and understand further steps. This important tool can help demonstrate the business case that investing in the health and wellbeing of your workforce will increase productivity as well as staff engagement.

3.55 Dame Carol Black's *Working for a Healthier Tomorrow*[102] review highlighted that working-age ill health was costing England £100 billion a year. Key issues identified include early intervention and prevention, and proactive responses such as health-promoting workplaces, better mental health and employment outcomes, building young people's resilience and lengthening healthy working lives. Effectively addressing health, work and wellbeing provides the potential to reduce inequalities through increased economic prosperity, greater stability and viability of local communities.

Workplace Cycle Challenge

CTC, the national cyclists' organisation, has led a pilot project to encourage people to cycle to work in Swindon as part of its Cycling Champions programme.

The Cycle Challenge works by encouraging and supporting existing cyclists to persuade colleagues who rarely or never cycle to give it a try. The Challenge was a competition open to all organisations in the Swindon area to get the most staff to cycle for just 10 minutes or more. Whole organisations and individual workplaces were encouraged to sign up via the Challenge website – individual cyclists within those organisations could log their personal details and record how much cycling they did.

Overall, 853 participants cycled 37,180 miles between them, of which around 35,000 miles were for transport purposes (i.e. non-recreational travel). It is estimated that they saved 3,157 litres of fuel and £3,630 in reduced motoring costs and burnt 35 million kilojoules of energy.

www.swindoncyclechallenge.org.uk

3.56 With more than 1.4 million staff, the NHS is the largest employer in the UK and can lead by example in looking after the health and wellbeing of its staff. To support this, the Department of Health commissioned Dr Steve Boorman's report on the health and wellbeing of NHS staff. As a result, there is now a pledge in the NHS Constitution to provide support and opportunities for staff to maintain their health, wellbeing and safety. All NHS organisations are putting in place a local health and wellbeing strategy in 2010/11, including being proactive in improving the quality of and speeding up access to occupational health services, and strengthening board accountability for the management of sickness and absence. The NHS is working towards achieving a one-third reduction in sickness absence, which could release up to £555 million a year in efficiency savings.

Ageing well

3.57 All western countries are experiencing rapidly ageing populations. This is a major challenge for health and care systems typically geared to treating short-term sickness, not preventing and managing long-term mental and physical conditions in later life. As individuals grow older, key moments such as retirement or bereavement can be a catalyst to decline.

3.58 However, this decline is not an inevitable part of ageing. Public health will have a major leadership role in prevention, promoting active ageing and tackling inequalities. And by using the latest thinking from behavioural science, communities can be better designed to enable active ageing to become the norm rather than the exception.

3.59 Local government's new role in public health presents an opportunity to address this challenge. Public health will be better integrated with areas such as social care, transport, leisure, planning and housing, keeping people connected, active, independent and in their own homes. Neighbourhoods and houses can be better designed to support people's health, such as by creating Lifetime Homes, and by maintaining benefits such as the winter fuel allowance and free bus travel, which keep people active and reduce isolation.

3.60 Strong partnerships between communities, business and the voluntary sector will help address a range of health challenges such as depression and winter deaths. For example, the Department of Energy and Climate Change will develop a Green Deal across sectors to improve the energy efficiency and warmth of homes from 2012, alongside the new Energy Company Obligation. The Obligation will run in parallel with the Green Deal, and will focus particularly on the needs of the most vulnerable and on those in hard-to-heat homes, who will need the most additional support. We will enable older people themselves to contribute and participate more through families, communities and work, which also protects their own physical and mental health.

3.61 The population of rural England is ageing faster than that of urban areas. Sparse older rural populations can present challenges in terms of more limited social networks, transport issues and restricted access to services.

Gloucestershire Village Agents – a rural volunteer network addressing exclusion

Gloucestershire County Council, supported by the Department for Work and Pensions, has developed a scheme of 'Village Agents', volunteers who identify and work with excluded older people to build community capacity. Village Agents are trusted local people, supported by a multi-agency contact centre with links to services for health, social care, housing, personal safety and benefits.

The 2007 evaluation showed that 30 Village Agents made 20,000 contacts with local older people and that there were 2,500 formal referrals. Village Agents helped older people to claim over £300,000 in benefit entitlements, addressing pensioner poverty and supporting the rural economy. The evaluation showed cost-effective impacts on mental health, falls prevention and home safety.

Village Agents have expanded to cover 205 of the 253 parishes in Gloucestershire, and other areas have launched their own versions, including in Essex, Bath and North East Somerset, Leicestershire and Rutland, Northamptonshire and Warwickshire.

www.gloucestershire.gov.uk

3.62 We want to create an environment that supports people in making healthy choices, and that makes these choices easier. On housing, for example, the Lifetime Homes Standard remains an important part of the Code for Sustainable Homes encouraging development of more homes that are accessible and that meet the needs of an ageing population. The Warm Front scheme will also continue until 2012/13, providing grants to improve housing warmth and sustainability.

3.63 Local government provides a range of services to promote active ageing and help people live independently in their homes. We are committed to keeping older people in their homes longer through funding home adaptations and are maintaining programmes such as Supporting People, the Disabled Facilities Grant and Decent Homes, which keep homes safe and in good condition. Local government will also become more closely linked with the NHS through its role in supporting reablement through social care; and district nurses and allied health professionals will contribute to keeping people at home through falls prevention, nutritional advice and using community resources to prevent isolation.

3.64 Carers also play a vital role in supporting people to stay at home. The Department of Health carers' strategy sets out how we will support carers to recognise the value of their contribution, involve them in how care is delivered, support their mental and physical health and enable them to have a work, family and community life. As part of this, the Government is making an additional £400 million available through the NHS over the next four years to support carers' breaks.

3.65 The Government's vision for adult social care sets out the ambition to increase preventive action, keeping people active and independent in the community. Additional resources have been made available from within the health system to support social care services, such as evidence-based preventive services. At local level, Directors of Public Health (DsPH) and Directors of Adult Social Services will be able to work together to commission specific services for older people and those who care for them. These could range from services such as information and advice, through to case-finding for at-risk individuals, delivery of appropriate immunisations and services aimed at minimising disability, deterioration or dependency.

3.66 However, we also need to change social norms and attitudes. Ageist attitudes and practices have a detrimental effect on older people, both directly and through their take-up of services. The Equality Act 2010 will prohibit age discrimination against people aged 18 and over when providing a service or exercising a public function; this affects the Department of Health, the NHS and social care bodies. These provisions will come into force in 2012. The Act also includes a new public sector Equality Duty covering eight protected equality characteristics, including age, which comes into effect in April 2011.

3.67 Local government and central government will work in partnership with businesses, voluntary groups and older people in creating opportunities to become active, remain socially connected, and play an active part in communities – avoiding social isolation and loneliness. For example, Older People's Day on 1 October aims to change attitudes to ageing. This has become a real community movement which celebrates later life and this year included over 3,000 events across the country.

3.68 The Department for Work and Pensions will provide Active@60 grants to voluntary and community groups to establish Community Agents in their area. Volunteers will work with people typically in their 60s to help them make a good start to their later life. They will reach out to those at risk of isolation and exclusion. The Community Agent role has been developed with people from the target group, and draws on the latest behavioural science thinking to help tackle social exclusion.

3.69 We will maintain and improve the standard of living of older people. We are committed to phasing out the default retirement age, allowing employers to use retirement ages of 65 or higher. This will allow people who otherwise would have been prevented from working longer to do so and means that they will be able to maintain the health and social benefits of working. We will also maintain the value of the state pension through the triple guarantee – the basic state pension will increase by the highest of the growth in average earnings, prices or 2.5%.

3.70 The taboo about discussing death and dying means that too many people can reach this critical point of their life unprepared, without having thought about how or where they would like to be cared for. This in turn affects their family and carers as a poor death can lead to a traumatic bereavement, with associated mental and physical health issues. The Department of Health will continue to promote the implementation of the End of Life Care Strategy and in particular the societal strand being led by the National Council for Palliative Care and the Dying Matters national coalition.

A new public health system

3.71 In the next chapter, we outline the Government's proposals for a new public health system which will provide opportunities to forge partnerships for children, working-age adults and older people to improve health and wellbeing throughout life.

4. A new public health system with strong local and national leadership

Summary

Localism will be at the heart of this new system, with devolved responsibilities, freedoms and funding. Directors of Public Health will be the strategic leaders for public health and health inequalities in local communities, working in partnership with the local NHS and across the public, private and voluntary sectors. The Government will shortly publish a response to the recent consultation on proposed new local statutory health and wellbeing boards to support collaboration across NHS and local authorities to meet communities' needs as effectively as possible.

A new, dedicated, professional public health service – Public Health England – will be set up as part of the Department of Health, which will strengthen the national response on emergency preparedness and health protection.

There will be ring-fenced public health funding from within the overall NHS budget to ensure that it is not squeezed by other pressures, for example NHS finances, although it will still be subject to the running-cost reductions and efficiency gains that will be required across the system. Early estimates suggest that current spend on the areas that are likely to be the responsibility of Public Health England could be over £4 billion.

There will be ring-fenced budgets for upper-tier and unitary local authorities and a new health premium to reward progress made locally against elements of the new proposed public health outcomes framework, taking into account health inequalities.

The new system will use the best evidence and evaluation and will support innovative approaches to behaviour change – with a new National Institute for Health Research (NIHR) School for Public Health Research and a Policy Research Unit on Behaviour and Health. There will be greater transparency, with data on health outcomes published nationally and locally.

> **Public health will be part of the NHS Commissioning Board's mandate, with public health support for NHS commissioning nationally and locally. There will be stronger incentives for GPs so that they play an active role in public health.**
>
> **The Chief Medical Officer will have a central role in providing independent advice to the Secretary of State for Health and the Government on the population's health. He or she will be the leading advocate for public health within, across and beyond government, and will lead a professional network for all those responsible for commissioning or providing public health.**
>
> **The core elements of the new system will be set out in the forthcoming Health and Social Care Bill, and are therefore subject to Parliament's approval.**

A new public health system: overview

4.1   To meet the challenges set out in earlier chapters, the Secretary of State for Health intends to create a new public health system in England to protect and improve the public's health, improving the health of the poorest, fastest.

4.2   For the first time in a generation, local government will be given the responsibility, backed by ring-fenced budgets and new freedoms, to make a major impact on improving people's health and tackling health inequalities in every community. Top-down targets will be replaced by a new outcomes framework. Directors of Public Health (DsPH) in upper-tier local government and unitary local authorities will lead these efforts, building on the important existing role of local government in public health. We will shortly publish our response to the consultation on proposed local statutory health and wellbeing boards in order to bring together NHS and local government efforts to meet the local population's needs as effectively as possible.

4.3   This will be backed up by a new, dedicated and professional public health service, known as Public Health England, within the Department of Health. Public Health England will bring together a fragmented system; it will do nationally what needs to be done; it will have a new protected public health budget; and it will support local action through funding and the provision of evidence, data and professional leadership. This new service will lead health protection, and harness the efforts of the whole of government, the NHS and the Big Society to improve the public's health.

4.4   The creation of Public Health England, and the strengthening of the role of local government in public health, must not lead to the NHS stepping back from its crucial role in public health. Enabling access to good health services that prevent avoidable illness – including by reaching out to disadvantaged, vulnerable and excluded groups – is crucial throughout people's lives. The NHS has a critical role to play in emergency preparedness and response, and in promoting health and preventing avoidable illness. This will be reflected in the mandate to the new NHS Commissioning Board (NHSCB) and legislation. There will need to be close partnership working between Public Health England and the NHS at a national level, and between local government, DsPH and GP consortia at the local level.

4.5 The Department of Health is designing the new system based on principles of empowering people, using transparency to drive accountability, and ensuring that communities lead efforts to improve health wherever possible, using evidence-based services and innovations tied to evaluation.

A new role and freedoms for local government

4.6 Local government, including county, district and parish councils, already plays a significant role in protecting and improving the health of its communities, through, for example, environmental health, air quality, planning, transport and housing. Local councils (districts, in two-tier situations) will continue to carry out their statutory duties under the Public Health (Control of Disease) Act 1984, as they do today. These duties include appointing 'proper officers' for the purposes of the 1984 Act. Existing functions in local government that contribute to public health will continue to be funded through the local government grant.

4.7 Local leadership will be at the heart of the new public health system, with new ring-fenced budgets, enhanced freedoms and responsibilities for local government to improve the health and wellbeing of their population and reduce inequalities. The Health and Social Care Bill will provide that upper-tier and unitary local authorities will have a duty to take steps to improve the health of their population. It is proposed that these new functions would be conferred from 1 April 2013.

4.8 Embedding public health within local government will make it easier to create tailored local solutions in order to meet varying local needs. It will also enable joint approaches to be taken with other areas of local government's work (such as housing, the environment, transport, planning, children's services, social care, environmental health and leisure) and with key partners (such as the NHS, police, business, early years services, schools and voluntary organisations).

4.9 The Government will require DsPH to be employed in upper-tier councils (i.e. county councils) and unitary authorities (i.e. district councils, where there is no county council, and borough councils) to lead local public health efforts, a role that can be shared with other local councils if agreed locally. We will keep to a minimum the constraints as to how local government decides to fulfil its public health role and spend its new budget. There will be payment for progress made against elements of the public health outcomes framework.

Local government: joining up local approaches to health and wellbeing

4.10 The Department of Health recently consulted on proposals for local statutory health and wellbeing boards, which will bring together the key NHS, public health and social care leaders in each local authority area to work in partnership. The health and wellbeing board would be able establish a shared local view about the needs of the community and support joint commissioning of NHS, social care and public health services in order to meet the needs of the whole local population effectively. Responses to the consultation have been generally very supportive of local statutory health and wellbeing boards, with a desire to see clarity of accountability in the system between local authorities, GP consortia and the NHSCB. Local government and the NHS have also wanted to see close partnership working and joined-up commissioning strategies between the NHS and local authorities. The Department of Health is taking these views into account in developing final proposals and will shortly publish the full consultation response.

4.11 However, we can confirm that we will put forward detailed proposals for the establishment of health and wellbeing boards in every upper-tier local authority. They will also have the flexibility to bring in the local expertise of district councils. There will be a proposed minimum membership of elected representatives, GP consortia, DsPH, Directors of Adult Social Services, Directors of Children's Services, local HealthWatch and, where appropriate, the participation of the NHSCB. Subject to legislation, these members will be required to be part of the board, and local areas will be able to expand membership to include local voluntary groups, clinicians and providers, where appropriate. GP consortia and local authorities, including DsPH, will each have an equal and explicit obligation to prepare the Joint Strategic Needs Assessment (JSNA), and to do so through the arrangements made by the health and wellbeing board.

4.12 The Department of Health has also proposed a new role for local government to encourage coherent commissioning strategies, promoting the development of integrated and joined up commissioning plans across the NHS, social care, public health and other local partners. Ultimately, this should deliver better health and wellbeing outcomes, better quality of care, and better value for money, with fewer overlaps or gaps in provision, and different services working sensibly together.

4.13 We envisage health and wellbeing boards developing joint health and wellbeing strategies, based on the assessment of need outlined in their JSNA, and including a consideration of how all the relevant commissioners can work together. It is expected that this local, joint health and wellbeing strategy will provide the overarching framework within which more detailed and specific commissioning plans for the NHS, social care, public health, and other services that the health and wellbeing board agrees to consider, are developed. We would encourage organisations to develop concise and high-level strategies setting out how they will address the health and wellbeing needs of a community, rather than large, technical documents duplicating other plans. The joint health and wellbeing strategy would have to include consideration of whether existing flexibilities to pool budgets and joined-up commissioning can be used to deliver the strategy.

4.14 There is huge potential to meet people's needs more effectively and promote the best use of public resources through close working relationships between local authorities and the NHS, to further integrate health with adult social care, children's services (including education) and wider services, including disability services, housing, and criminal justice agencies. There will be sufficient flexibility in the legislative framework for health and wellbeing boards to go beyond their minimum statutory duties to promote joining-up of a much broader range of local services for the benefit of their local populations' health and wellbeing.

4.15 Many areas are developing their own locally agreed partnership arrangements, such as public service boards and Community Budgets, to support this kind of collaboration and agree shared outcomes that health, local government, the police and others will set out to achieve in partnership with local communities.

4.16 Local authorities are free to take joint approaches to public health where they think that is the best way to tackle health improvement challenges that extend beyond local areas. For example, in response to the consultation on the NHS White Paper, *Equity and Excellence: Liberating the NHS*, the Mayor of London has made the case for a city-wide approach in London. The Secretary of State has invited the Mayor and local authorities in London to develop proposals on how they can collectively work together to improve health in London – and is open to proposals for joint working in other areas of the country.

Local government: promoting public health

4.17 DsPH will be employed by local government and jointly appointed by the relevant local authority and Public Health England. They will be the strategic leaders for public health in local communities, working to achieve the best possible public health and wellbeing outcomes across the whole local population, in accordance with locally agreed priorities. They will be professionally accountable to the Chief Medical Officer (CMO) and part of the Public Health England professional network.

4.18 The DPH will be a public health professional, with the training, expertise and skills needed to enable them to meet both the leadership and technical requirements of the role. They would be expected to maintain their professional skills.

4.19 Subject to the passage of the Health and Social Care Bill, DsPH will be responsible for the health improvement functions of upper-tier and unitary authorities and will be required to prepare an annual report on the population's health. To meet these responsibilities, DsPH will need to discharge their functions in a number of ways, ranging from direct responsibility for achieving public health outcomes to advising colleagues and partners on public health. They will need to be supported by a team with specific public health and commissioning expertise.

4.20 To be the most effective leaders possible of public health in their areas, DsPH will have a number of critical tasks, set out in more detail in the Annex, including:

- promoting health and wellbeing within local government;

- providing and using evidence relating to health and wellbeing;

- advising and supporting GP consortia on the population aspects of NHS services;

- developing an approach to improving health and wellbeing locally, including promoting equality and tackling health inequalities;

- working closely with Public Health England health protection units (HPUs) to provide health protection as directed by the Secretary of State for Health; and

- collaborating with local partners on improving health and wellbeing, including GP consortia, other local DsPH, local businesses and others.

4.21 There are various models for how effective public health services can be delivered, and it should be determined locally as to how particular areas make their arrangements.

4.22 To make a reality of localism and local democracy, local government must have the freedom to decide what action is needed to take in order to shape their environments. For example, local planning authorities already have the ability to regulate the development of new fast food restaurants, and to impose conditions on such development, for example, to specify the operating hours. In addition, the proposed new 'general power of competence' will provide them with much greater freedom and flexibility to act in the interest of their communities.

4.23 These freedoms open up opportunities for local government to take innovative approaches to public health by involving new partners. We will encourage local authorities who may want to contract for services with a wide range of providers across the public, private and voluntary sectors and to incentivise and reward those organisations to deliver the best outcomes for their population. The forthcoming consultation on funding and commissioning in public health will explore how this would best be achieved. As part of building capable and confident communities, areas may wish to consider grant funding for local communities to take ownership of some highly focused preventive activities, such as volunteering peer support, befriending and social networks.

4.24 The Department of Health expects that the majority of services will be commissioned, given the opportunities this would bring to engage local communities more widely in the provision of public health, to deliver best value and best results. It also expects that local people will have access to information about commissioning decisions and how public health money is being spent.

4.25 Such efforts will be supported by the proposed new right for communities to bid to take over local state-run services, and the new Big Society Bank, which will lever in new social investment for charities and social enterprises, helping to create an environment in which innovative approaches to social investment and social enterprise flourish.

4.26 The following sections outline the proposed funding and commissioning arrangements and the outcomes framework for public health, and how these relate to Public Health England. Further detail will be set out in the forthcoming consultation documents.

Funding and commissioning for public health

4.27 The Department of Health will shortly publish a consultation following this White Paper on the details of the proposed funding and commissioning routes for public health. This consultation includes the funding and commissioning remit that the Department proposes for Public Health England in the future. We welcome views on the proposals.

National public health budget

4.28 The new system will be funded by a new public health budget, which will be ring-fenced within the overall NHS budget. The Department will work to ensure that funding for public health is not squeezed by other pressures, for example NHS finances, although it will still be subject to the running-cost reductions and efficiency gains that will be required across the system.

4.29 The Government announced in the Spending Review that total NHS spending would grow cumulatively in cash terms by 10.3% by 2014/15. Early estimates suggest that current spend on areas that are likely to be the responsibility of Public Health England could be over £4 billion. This estimate will be revised as the detailed design of Public Health England develops and we gather more information about existing services and spend.

4.30 Determining the baseline spend on the relevant areas is the first step in establishing the future public health budget, wherever possible taking account of any disruption caused by the transition to new NHS structures.

Local public health budget

4.31 Public Health England will allocate ring-fenced budgets, weighted for inequalities, to upper-tier and unitary authorities in local government for improving the health and wellbeing of local populations. The ring-fenced budgets will fund both improving population health and wellbeing, and some non-discretionary services, such as open-access sexual health services and certain immunisations. There will be scope, as now, to pool budgets locally in order to support public health work.

4.32 To incentivise action to reduce health inequalities we will introduce a new health premium, which will apply to the part of the local public health budget which is for health improvement. Building on a baseline allocation that is weighted towards areas with the worst health outcomes and most need, local authorities will receive an incentive payment, or premium, for these services that depends on the progress made in improving the health of the local population, based on elements of the proposed outcomes framework.

4.33 The premium will be simple and driven by a formula developed with key partners. Disadvantaged areas will see a greater premium if they make progress, recognising that they face the greatest challenges.

4.34 The health premium will be funded from within the overall public health budget. Potentially, an area that makes no progress might receive no growth in funding for these services. We intend the support for progress in reducing health inequalities to be clear and significant.

4.35 The forthcoming consultation document will discuss further some of the issues we will need to consider when developing the health premium, to allow more detailed discussions with local authorities and public health professionals. We will only set out a detailed model when we have established the baseline and potential scale of the premium clearly, and have agreement about the outcomes we will use.

4.36 The Department of Health will ask the independent Advisory Committee on Resource Allocation (ACRA) to support the detailed development of its approach to allocating resources to local authorities.

4.37 The public health grant to local authorities will be made under section 31 of the Local Government Act 2003. As a ring-fenced grant, it will carry some conditions about how the budget is to be used. However, we will seek to enable flexibility for local areas to determine how best they can use this funding to improve the health and wellbeing of their community.

4.38 There will be 'shadow' allocations to local authorities for each local area for this budget in 2012/13, providing an opportunity for planning before allocations are introduced in 2013/14. During the transitional year, 2011/12, the forthcoming NHS Operating Framework for 2011/12 will set out the operational arrangements to manage the transition and will continue to signal the importance of NHS action on health improvement, health protection, preventing ill health and improving wellbeing. The NHS Operating Framework will set the context for the running-cost reductions and efficiency gains required across the system.

Commissioning of public health services

4.39 Public Health England will fund those services that contribute to health and wellbeing primarily by prevention rather than treatment aimed at cure. It will do so in a way that takes account of and addresses the needs of the whole population, including all protected characteristics as set out in the Equality Act 2010 (i.e. age, disability, gender reassignment, race, religion or belief, sex, sexual orientation, marriage and civil partnership, pregnancy and maternity).

4.40 Using these criteria, we propose that Public Health England should be responsible for funding and ensuring the provision of services such as health protection, emergency preparedness, recovery from drug dependency, sexual health, immunisation programmes, alcohol prevention, obesity, smoking cessation, nutrition, health checks, screening, child health promotion including those led by health visiting and school nursing, and some elements of the GP contract (including the Quality and Outcomes Framework (QOF)) such as those relating to immunisation, contraception, and dental public health. Full proposals will be set out in the forthcoming consultation document.

4.41 Public Health England will have three principal routes for funding services:

- granting the public health ring-fenced budget to local government;

- asking the NHSCB to commission services, such as screening services, and the relevant elements of the GP contract; and

- commissioning or providing services directly, for example national purchasing of vaccines, national communication campaigns, or health protection functions currently conducted by the Health Protection Agency (HPA).

4.42 These are not exclusive; for example, if appropriate, there may be an option for GP consortia to commission on behalf of Public Health England. Figure 4.1 gives an overview of the three principal routes for commissioning public health services in the future. For simplicity, this diagram only considers major routes of funding and accountability, and does not include, for example, funding to local authorities from other government departments.

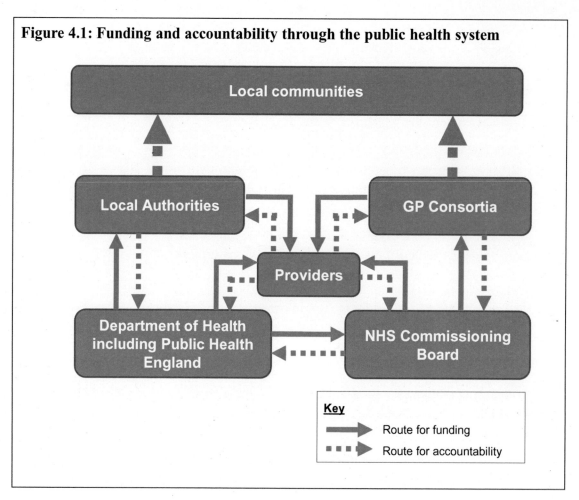

Figure 4.1: Funding and accountability through the public health system

For further details and consultation questions, see the forthcoming consultation on funding and commissioning of public health.

4.43 Given the crucial role that early years development plays in setting up children for a healthy life, health visiting, school nursing and the child health promotion services they lead, in particular the Healthy Child Programme, will be funded from the Public Health England budget. In the first instance, the Department of Health and then the NHSCB will lead the commissioning of health visiting services on behalf of Public Health England, to oversee the workforce growth needed to meet the Coalition commitment to a further 4,200 health visitors. The NHSCB will work closely with PCTs, GP consortia and their local partners. It will be important to ensure that local mechanisms such as the proposed statutory local health and wellbeing board and the JSNA are used to enable high-quality public health input into the commissioning of health visiting services. These will help to strengthen and maintain the critical links with other services such as local authority commissioned early years' services like children's centres, as well as with other NHS services such as maternity and primary care. In the longer term, we expect health visiting to be commissioned locally. These changes to commissioning do not affect the employment arrangements for health visitors being taken forward under Transforming Community Services. The Department of Health will publish a plan setting out how this commitment will be taken forward over the next five years.

Public health outcomes framework

4.44 Chapter 2 set out the purpose and proposed outline for the new public health outcomes framework, which will be complementary to those for the NHS and social care and which will drive improvements in public health throughout the new system. It will set out a high-level vision and outcomes, along with a number of possible indicators across five domains, reflecting the breadth of Public Health England's mission. To enable transparency and accountability, outcomes will be published nationally and, where possible, locally.

4.45 The Department of Health has been working closely with partners to develop proposals for a public health outcomes framework. We will publish a consultation on this shortly. We welcome your views on this.

For further details and consultation questions, see the forthcoming consultation on the proposed public health outcomes framework.

National-level partnership with the NHS

4.46 The NHS has a crucial continuing role to play in public health. This includes ensuring that health services meet the needs of the whole population, including disadvantaged groups, taking every opportunity that health services have to prevent illness and promote health, and playing a critical part in preparing for and responding to emergencies.

4.47 The work of Public Health England will also benefit the NHS, by reducing pressures from avoidable illnesses and allowing the NHS to focus its efforts elsewhere. If Public Health England can help to reduce obesity, for example, we should see lower levels of diabetes and liver disease. By reducing the number of people who smoke, the NHS should not need to keep spending £2.7 billion a year on treating smoking related illness.[103] The QIPP (Quality, Innovation, Productivity and Prevention) programme was initiated and is driven by the NHS and includes savings from prevention such as smoking cessation and reducing alcohol harm.

4.48 There will need to be close partnership working between Public Health England and the NHS at a national level. The NHS role will be embedded in the mandate that the Secretary of State sets for the NHSCB. Public Health England will be able to advise and support the wider Department of Health and the NHS nationally in this role, to ensure that health services meet the needs of the whole population.

4.49 The Coalition agreement *The Coalition: our programme for government*[104] announced that the Department of Health will strengthen the role and incentives for GPs and GP practices on preventive services – both as primary care professionals and as commissioners. As primary care professionals, GPs and GP practices play a critical role in both primary and secondary care prevention. They have huge opportunities to provide advice, brief interventions and referral to targeted services through the millions of contacts they have with patients each year.

4.50 As NHS commissioners, GP consortia will have responsibility for the whole population in their area, including registered patients, unregistered citizens and visitors requiring urgent care. This should encourage them to work with local authorities and a diverse range of clinicians, including nurses, midwives, health visitors, allied health professionals, pharmacists and dentists, to improve the health of the local population as a whole.

4.51 The Department of Health will work to strengthen the public health role of GPs in the following ways:

- Public Health England and the NHSCB will work together to support and encourage GP consortia to maximise their impact on improving population health and reducing health inequalities. This will include looking specifically at equitable access to services and outcomes.

- Information on achievement by practices will be available publicly, supporting people to choose their GP practice based on performance. By increasing transparency about how effective different GP practices are in giving public health advice, Public Health England will enable local communities to challenge GPs to enhance their performance.

- Incentives and drivers for GP-led activity will be designed with public health concerns in mind, for example, in terms of prevention-related measures in the QOF. To increase the incentives for GP practices to improve the health of their patients, the Department proposes that a sum at least equivalent to 15% of the current value of the QOF should be devoted to evidence-based public health and primary prevention indicators from 2013. The funding for this element of QOF will be within the Public Health England budget.

- Public Health England will strengthen the focus on public health issues in the education and training of GPs, as part of the Department of Health's development of a workforce strategy.

Consultation question: Role of GPs and GP practices in public health

a. Are there additional ways in which we can ensure that GPs and GP practices will continue to play a key role in areas for which Public Health England will take responsibility?

4.52 Community pharmacies are a valuable and trusted public health resource. With millions of contacts with the public each day, there is real potential to use community pharmacy teams more effectively to improve health and wellbeing and reduce health inequalities. Public Health England will influence development of the community pharmacy contractual framework through the NHSCB. Alongside identifying strategic health needs through JSNAs, local authorities, through proposed health and wellbeing boards, will have responsibility for producing pharmaceutical needs assessments, which will inform the commissioning of community pharmacy services by the NHSCB and local public health commissioning decisions. We will build on this as we establish the new system, with the Chief Pharmaceutical Officer working closely with the public health community. This will include the role of pharmacies as local businesses and employers.

4.53 The dental public health workforce will increase its focus on effective health promotion and prevention of oral disease, provision of evidence-based oral care and effective dental clinical governance. It will concentrate particularly on improving children's oral health, because those who have healthy teeth in childhood have every chance of keeping good oral health throughout their lives. It will also make a vital contribution to implementation of a new contract for primary care dentistry, which the Government is to introduce to increase emphasis on prevention while meeting patients' treatment needs more effectively.

National leadership and responsibilities

4.54 As the Department of Health is freed from the operational management of the NHS, it will refocus efforts on protecting and improving the health and wellbeing of England as a whole. Enhanced central powers will only be taken where absolutely necessary – this includes new powers for the Secretary of State to protect the population's health and to prepare for and respond to health threats that people and communities cannot tackle alone.

4.55 Within and beyond government, the Secretary of State for Health will do what needs to be done to protect health from external threats, will tackle the wider determinants of health and wellbeing, and will support local public health efforts.

4.56 The Secretary of State for Health's role will include:

- accounting to Parliament and the public for the Government's public health activities and spending;

- ensuring that the overall health and care system works coherently to deliver better health and wellbeing, better care and better value for the population and to address health inequalities;

- setting a ring-fenced budget for public health from within the overall NHS budget;

- setting the direction for Public Health England and the context for local public health efforts, through the public health outcomes framework;

- leading public health across central government, through the Cabinet Sub-Committee on Public Health;

- leading public health work across civil society and with business and brokering partnerships at national level with industry and the voluntary and community sectors to help drive behavioural change;

- participating in public health work across the UK with the Devolved Administrations and at European and international levels;

- proposing legislation where this is a necessary and appropriate response; and

- commissioning research for public health through the NIHR.

4.57 The CMO will have a central role in providing independent advice to the Secretary of State for Health and the Government on the population's health. He or she will be the leading advocate for public health within, across and beyond government, challenging industry, employers, and civil society to take a bigger role in and responsibility for the public's health. As convener and chair of a proposed new public health system advisory board, the CMO will bring together key partners to collaborate to improve and protect the public's health. The CMO will help to shape the role and expectations of local DsPH who will be professionally accountable to the CMO. The CMO will also lead a professional network for Public Health England.

4.58 On a wider front, the CMO will be expected to produce for publication an annual report 'On the State of the Public's Health', increasing transparency about the progress within public health, and helping to drive forward improvement across England. The CMO will also represent the UK internationally on public health issues.

A new streamlined Public Health England

4.59 For the first time ever, there will be a dedicated and professional public health service, Public Health England, with a mission across the whole of public health – protecting the public from health threats, improving the healthy life expectancy and wellbeing of the population, and improving the health of the poorest, fastest. It will work closely with the NHS to ensure that health services play a strong part in this mission, and it will support them in that task. It will bring together public health functions that are carried out in different parts of the system at present into a new, streamlined whole so as to remove duplication and drive efficiencies and innovation.

4.60 Public Health England will be part of the Department of Health, accountable to the Secretary of State for Health. It will not be a separate legal entity. Subject to the passage of the Health and Social Care Bill, it will include the current functions of the HPA and the NTA, which will become functions of the Secretary of State for Health. This will enhance the role of the Secretary of State for Health in health protection and will create an integrated system without artificial boundaries, or separate boards and accountabilities.

4.61 Public Health England will also include elements of public health activity currently held within the Department of Health and within strategic health authorities (SHAs) along with functions of the Public Health Observatories and cancer registries. It will work with local government, the NHS, other government agencies and other partners as necessary in preparing for and responding to emergency threats and in building partnerships for health.

4.62 Public Health England will be subject to the planned reduction of one-third of non-frontline administration costs across the whole system, while protecting frontline services. This will be managed within the overall human resources and financial framework of the Department of Health as part of its transition programme. The Department of Health will also set up an appropriate mechanism to ensure that the income generation activities of the HPA can be maintained.

4.63 Public Health England will have functions that need to be organised and aggregated at different levels to achieve maximum efficiency rather than the present mandated regional structure. In particular, managing health protection, especially emergency preparedness, will require strong links between Public Health England and the NHS, local government and others throughout the country. For example, infectious disease outbreaks often spread beyond the boundaries of a single local area, requiring co-ordinated management. Public Health England will therefore have an important local presence in the form of Health Protection Units (HPUs), working closely as now with the NHS and local government colleagues. Further details of this role are set out later in this chapter.

4.64 Public Health England's role will include:

- providing public health advice, evidence and expertise to the Secretary of State and the wider system, including working with partners to gather and disseminate examples of what works;

- delivering effective health protection services;

- commissioning or providing national-level health improvement services, including appropriate information and behaviour change campaigns;

- jointly appointing DsPH and supporting them through professional accountability arrangements;

- allocating ring-fenced funding to local government and rewarding them for progress made against elements of the proposed public health outcomes framework;

- commissioning some public health services from the NHS, for example via the NHSCB; and

- contributing internationally-leading science to the UK and globally, in areas such as biological standards and control, dangerous pathogens, and incident response.

4.65 Public Health England will maintain the principles and practice of independent scientific and public health advice, which are essential to maintain public and professional confidence and transparency. It will maintain a source of independent expert advice, including through a structure of Expert Committees, which will continue to operate according to the Government's Chief Scientific Adviser's guidance. Statistical publications will follow established procedures for release of official statistics. It will use the best available science as the basis for advice to the population, health professionals and others, for example in responding to incidents.

4.66 As is the case today, the NHS Constitution will continue to apply to the whole health service, whether the NHS or Public Health England. There is a wider social duty to promote equality through the services provided by the NHS and Public Health England, paying particular attention to groups or sections of society where improvement in health and life expectancy are not keeping pace with the rest of the population.

4.67 The Department of Health will work closely with the Devolved Administrations on UK-wide issues wherever appropriate, such as for biological standards and radiological protection. EU negotiations are conducted for the UK as a whole, and the Department of Health will carry these out in close consultation with the Devolved Administrations.

Enhanced protection for health

Emergency preparedness and response

4.68 The Government will devolve public health leadership wherever possible, but will keep powers and strengthen them where there is a strong case for central leadership. Preparing for and tackling emergencies to protect the population from events from which they cannot protect themselves is a core role that national government should perform.

4.69 Public Health England will build on the current arrangements for emergency preparedness, resilience and response. There will be a robust new system underpinned by powers held by the Secretary of State for Health, with streamlined Public Health England functions and assurance.

4.70 Public Health England and the NHS need to plan, prepare and be able to respond to a range of disruptive challenges – such as terrorism, infectious disease outbreaks, chemical, biological, radiological and nuclear incidents, and the health impacts of climate change – in a co-ordinated and effective way both nationally and locally.

4.71 Public Health England will bring together the health protection and emergency planning and response functions from the Department of Health, the HPA and SHAs. These functions will provide a high level of scientific expertise, available to all parts of Public Health England, to the NHS, to multi-agency partners, and to central and local government.

4.72 At a national level, the Secretary of State of Health will have powers of direction in the event of what he considers to be an emergency, including powers to direct NHS providers as to how they should respond. The Secretary of State will be able to delegate powers of direction over NHS providers to the NHSCB, which will be responsible for assuring NHS preparedness and resilience, by assuring that clear arrangements are in place, services are co-ordinated and there are designated lead individuals. In the event of an emergency, the NHSCB will have responsibility for mobilising the NHS.

4.73 In the response phase, there will be national leadership, with most incidents managed locally by the Public Health England HPUs and local DsPH working together. Public Health England and the NHS will be part of the multi-agency local response, and it will be important that they plan and respond together.

4.74 The Department of Health will ensure that capacity for emergency preparedness and response is maintained throughout the transition to these new arrangements.

Health protection services

4.75 Health protection is concerned with infectious and environmental hazards (including radiation, chemicals, poisons, air pollution and the health effects of climate change) that affect people often in circumstances that are not easily avoidable.

4.76 In addition to emergency preparedness and response, a range of health protection functions are best done at a national level to ensure that the Government is protecting the population from threats. Public Health England will:

- provide a coherent, accountable national framework for rapid responses to threats;

- act in co-ordination across government and with other national partners in response to public health threats;

- provide evidence-gathering and surveillance functions, supported by scientific expertise;

- provide information and independent advice on hazards to health to professionals and the public;

- provide specialist and reference microbiology functions;

- set the standards for the national immunisation programme, advised by the independent Joint Committee on Vaccinations and Immunisations, and centrally procure many vaccines;

- commission communication campaigns where needed; and

- respond to legislative requirements including those set by the EU such as on emission levels.

4.77 Local government already works hard to protect health, for example, with environmental health officers playing a vital role during infectious disease outbreaks. In addition, the HPA has HPUs sited around the country. These are front-line delivery units, which include specialist public health and clinical staff, and provide the critical response to incidents, alongside monitoring and surveillance to protect the public's health. In the future, Public Health England will continue to work closely with local government in delivering health protection through HPUs.

Evidence for public health

4.78 In light of the Government's commitment to doing what works, Public Health England will promote information-led, knowledge-driven public health interventions – supporting national and local public health efforts. The Department of Health will develop an evidence-based approach to public health alongside an evidence-based approach to healthcare. As the Government considers the challenges of the future, it will need to develop and enhance the public health evidence base. It will champion new approaches such as those offered by behavioural science, and develop and provide clear, practical evidence on how to influence the wider determinants of health.

4.79 Public Health England offers a unique opportunity to draw together the existing complex information, intelligence and surveillance functions performed by multiple organisations into a more coherent form and to make evidence more easily available to those who will use it, in a form that makes it most likely to be used.

4.80 Local requirements for public health evidence will drive Public Health England's evidence function, ensuring it is responsive to local needs and accessible to users across the country. DsPH, front-line teams, commissioners of NHS and public health services, public and patient representatives and wider partners will all benefit from enhanced public health evidence. By ensuring a strong central information and intelligence function, Public Health England will support the specialist workforce required to meet local requirements effectively and efficiently.

4.81 Public health practitioners from all sectors, including healthcare, the voluntary and community sector, and academia, will be critical in developing innovative and structured approaches, enabling evaluation and sharing the evidence from evaluation, thus driving the agenda for public health evidence development.

4.82 The best way to ensure that the new system is effective and cost-efficient in its approach to public health is by providing people with transparent information on the cost, the evidence-base and, ultimately, the impact of services. The new system, particularly Public Health England and local government, will provide information to the public about how taxpayers' money is being used and the outcomes it is achieving.

4.83 Public Health England's approach to evidence will be based on three principles:

- quality – evidence will be timely, reliable, relevant to the audience and aim, and produced in a scientifically robust and independent way;

- transparency – evidence will be as accessible and user-friendly as possible, driving accountability through increased availability of information. This will be in line with the Government's commitment to create a new 'right to data' so that government-held datasets can be requested and used by the public, underpinned by the Transparency Board's Public Data Principles;[105] and

- efficiency – information will be collected once but used many times and new knowledge will be rapidly applied as it becomes available.

Research

4.84 Public health evaluation and research will be critical in enabling public health practice to develop into the future and address key challenges and opportunities, such as how to handle the wider determinants of health and how to use behaviour change science to support better practice. At the basis of this is the need to try new ideas and innovate in a structured manner.

4.85 The NIHR will continue to take responsibility for the commissioning of public health research on behalf of the Department of Health, working with partners whose actions affect public health. Public Health England will work closely with the NIHR in identifying research priorities. To further develop public health research the Department will:

- establish an NIHR School for Public Health Research – conducting high-quality research to increase the evidence base for effective public health practice. This school will draw on leading academic centres with excellence in applied public health research and evaluations and place emphasis on what works practically and can be applied across the whole country;

- continue to promote a public health focus within the NIHR and fund, from within the Department's Policy Research Programme, a new Policy Research Unit on Behaviour and Health; and

- ensure that Public Health England provides the necessary resource to support the cost of public health interventions that are undergoing research outside of the NHS.

Information and intelligence

4.86 As the Department of Health designs and develops the future public health system, it will continue working closely with the full range of public health partners involved in surveillance, monitoring, evaluation and intelligence in order to develop a clear approach for information and intelligence. In the coming year, the Department will focus on drawing together existing public health information and intelligence functions (for example, the Public Health Observatories, cancer registries, and relevant parts of the HPA), working to eliminate gaps and overlaps and to develop the specialist workforce required.

4.87 Once established, Public Health England will:

- strengthen public health surveillance by ensuring fit-for-purpose data collection and analysis of health outcomes, providing early warning of problems and enabling a rapid and effective public health response;

- work with and measure the impact of different communications channels, including NHS Choices, to ensure that we provide a single, trusted source of information during public health emergencies, as well as supporting individuals to make informed lifestyle choices;

- ensure that the National Institute for Health and Clinical Excellence (NICE) adds maximum value by providing authoritative, independent advice on the evidence of effectiveness and cost effectiveness for public health interventions, working to specific commissions from Public Health England; and

- develop intelligence about the relative cost effectiveness of different interventions to support DsPH in commissioning local services, building on the work already started by NICE.[106]

4.88 The Department wants to consult those interested in public health practice on the best way of developing public health evidence in the future, with particular interest in comments on the following proposals:

- publishing an annual review of the latest evidence on what works best in achieving better public health outcomes;

- developing a single, accessible and authoritative web-based evidence system for professionals, particularly DsPH, to make evidence easily available to all and to encourage the use of the best evidence in practice; and

- encouraging recognition and peer-sharing of successful innovative evidence-based approaches.

Consultation questions: Public health evidence

b. **What are the best opportunities to develop and enhance the availability, accessibility and utility of public health information and intelligence?**

c. **How can Public Health England address current gaps such as using the insights of behavioural science, tackling wider determinants of health, achieving cost effectiveness and tackling inequalities?**

d. **What can wider partners nationally and locally contribute to improving the use of evidence in public health?**

Workforce for public health

4.89 The Government wants to build on the achievements and skills of the current public health workforce. Maintaining a well-trained, highly motivated public health workforce will be critical to the success of the public health system.

Our vision for the public health workforce

We envisage that the public health workforce will be known for its:

- expertise – public health staff, whatever their discipline and wherever they work, will be well-trained and expert in their field, committed to developing and maintaining that expertise and using an evidence-based approach to practice;

- professionalism – they will demonstrate the highest standards of professional conduct in their work;

- commitment to the population's health and wellbeing – in everything they do, they will focus on improving and protecting the health and wellbeing of their populations, taking account of equality and rights, whether it be a DPH in a local authority, an infection control nurse in an acute trust or a microbiologist within Public Health England; and

- flexibility – they will work effectively and in partnership across organisational boundaries.

4.90 Our vision for the future public health workforce is set out above. A more detailed workforce strategy to support this will be developed by autumn 2011, working with representative organisations. This will support a smooth and effective transition, informed by the views of people on the frontline of public health delivery.

4.91 The workforce strategy will set out how a supply of highly trained and motivated staff, with the appropriate skills for understanding the range of public health interventions, providing public health advice and commissioning the services communities require, can be sustained and grown, as needed.

4.92 In the future, a range of public health staff will work in Public Health England, employed by the Department of Health. These will include staff employed by the HPA, the NTA and the Department of Health.

4.93 Many critical roles in public health are played by people who will not be employed by Public Health England, but who will be part of a wider professional network. A very wide range of clinicians and other professionals – from GPs to dentists, pharmacists to nurses, allied health professionals to environmental health officers – have essential roles to play in improving and protecting population health and reducing health inequalities.

4.94 After completion of Transforming Community Services in April 2011, the provider functions of PCTs will have moved to other organisations, including community foundation trusts and social enterprises. As set out in *Excellence and Equity: Liberating the NHS* (2010), there will be a move to 'any willing provider' for community services to improve choice and access for local people. This White Paper does not change the direction of travel for local community services.

4.95 It is critical that scarce public health skills within the system are retained, including capacity to support senior leadership of the public health service. The Department of Health will therefore encourage PCTs and local government to discuss the future shape of public health locally. It is important to ensure that specialist staff, including medical and clinical staff, are rewarded fairly wherever they work; that their pay is properly governed locally; and that reasonable arrangements are in place to promote the flexibility and mobility of the workforce in the longer term. The Department of Health will work with the Local Government Association to consider what advice, support and guidance may be needed to support this. The Department will ensure that the human resources framework being developed with trade unions specifically addresses the development of Public Health England.

4.96 Alongside *Healthy Lives, Healthy People*, the Department of Health is publishing a review by Dr Gabriel Scally of the regulation of public health professionals. As the Government believes that statutory regulation should be a last resort, its preferred approach is to ensure effective and independently-assured voluntary regulation for any unregulated public health specialists. As professional regulation is a devolved matter, we will be consulting in all parts of the United Kingdom on this issue.

4.97 For other public health practitioners, the Department of Health will discuss with relevant groups the arrangements for setting and sustaining high standards of practice.

> **Consultation question: Regulation of public health professionals**
>
> **e. We would welcome views on Dr Gabriel Scally's report. If we were to pursue voluntary registration, which organisation would be best suited to provide a system of voluntary regulation for public health specialists?**

4.98 The Government will consult separately on proposals for a new framework for education and training for all clinical and healthcare professionals. The consultation will be based on the principle that the system should be focused on patient needs, driven by healthcare provider decisions and underpinned by strong clinical leadership. In designing a new system for the health sector, it will be important to ensure that there is alignment with the evolving Public Health England.

Conclusion

4.99 This new system – with localism at its heart, backed by national action where needed – will address the problems of the past and set England up to tackle the public health challenges of the future. We welcome views on the questions set out in this chapter during the consultation period. The following chapter sets out the consultation process, along with our proposed transition to the new system.

5. Making it happen

Summary

Subject to the passage of the Health and Social Care Bill, the Government plans to:

- **enable the creation of Public Health England, which will take on full responsibilities from 2012, including the formal transfer of functions and powers from the Health Protection Agency (HPA) and the National Treatment Agency for Substance Misuse (NTA);**

- **transfer local health improvement functions to local government, with ring-fenced funding allocated to local government from April 2013; and**

- **give local government new functions to increase local accountability and support integration and partnership working across social care, the NHS and public health.**

The transition to Public Health England will be developed in alignment with changes to primary care trusts (PCTs) and strategic health authorities (SHAs), and the creation of the NHS Commissioning Board (NHSCB). The detailed arrangements will be set out in a series of planning letters throughout the course of 2011.

A number of consultation questions are summarised in this chapter, and we would welcome your views on these questions. The consultation on these questions closes on 8 March 2011.

The Department of Health has published a review of the regulation of public health professionals by Dr Gabriel Scally. A consultation question about this is in Chapter 4 of this White Paper. We would welcome views on this report.

Forthcoming consultation documents will set out the proposed public health outcomes framework, and funding and commissioning arrangements for public health responsibilities.

5.1   This White Paper sets out the Government's strategy in the current Parliamentary term and beyond. This chapter sets out proposals for the transition to the new public health system in the context of wider changes to the health and social care system. It describes a phased approach that draws a clear distinction between the 'new' and the 'old', so that accountabilities and responsibilities are defined, enabling management teams to be put in place to build and prepare their organisations in advance of implementation, and to provide leadership across the system during transition.

5.2   As outlined in *Equity and Excellence: Liberating the NHS*, primary legislation will support the creation of Public Health England. The forthcoming Health and Social Care Bill will include these necessary reforms.

5.3   Much work now needs to be undertaken, both to manage the transition over the next two to three years, ensuring that the system continues to deliver a high-quality and safe service, and to develop the detail of the new system. This will be done alongside transition in other parts of the health and care sector, such as the creation of the NHSCB, GP consortia and proposed local statutory health and wellbeing boards.

5.4   The Department of Health will ensure that the system is robust and financially sustainable through the transition, as well as in the longer term. The effective management of health protection and emergency preparedness and response, as well as financial risk, will be of particular importance. The costs of transition and all the costs of policy commitments in this White Paper will be met within Departmental spending review allocations.

The transition to a new public health system

By early 2011

5.5   We will set out more detail on the proposed shape and structure of the new health and care system and our proposals for managing the transition in a series of publications in the coming months. These include:

- a detailed roadmap for the system as a whole – the NHS, Public Health England and the Department of Health – setting out the key transition milestones, expectations and activities for the years ahead;

- further detail on the public health system, based on our responses to the consultation in this White Paper and forthcoming consultations on funding and commissioning for public health and on the public health outcomes framework;

- human resources frameworks setting out the principles, expectations and approach for managing people moving between each of the organisations in the new health and care system;

- the Health and Social Care Bill, which will be introduced in Parliament following our response to the NHS White Paper consultations and will set out much greater detail on the structural and delivery implications of the system-wide reforms; and

- the NHS Operating Framework and the announcement of PCT allocations for 2011/12, which will be published in December 2010. These will set out expectations for the NHS during the first crucial transition year, including our expectations for public health delivery through PCTs.

5.6   The first step in determining budgets for public health will be to establish the baseline health spend on those services for which Public Health England will take responsibility in the future. Local PCT spending on such services during 2009/10 will be used as the baseline to reflect recent historic spending rather than spending during a transition year.

2011/12 – a year of transition

5.7   2011/12 will be a period of detailed policy and operational design, while transition to shadow bodies and planning for implementation take shape on the ground. We will continue to work closely with public health partners, local government and other stakeholders on the design of the new public health system throughout the passage of the Health and Social Care Bill and the consultation period for this White Paper and the forthcoming consultation documents.

5.8   There will be an overarching human resources framework with a common set of principles so that staff are treated fairly. One strand will cover all staff in the NHS affected by the changes set out in *Equity and Excellence: Liberating the NHS*. This will include all public health staff currently working in the NHS and those that will move to local authorities. Another strand will cover staff in the Department of Health. The third strand will cover staff in arm's-length bodies. The frameworks are designed to cover issues related to transfer and transition and the necessary functional support required by Public Health England as part of the Department of Health, including IT, communications, finance and estates.

5.9   In 2011, we will develop and consult on a public health workforce strategy, working with a wide range of employers and professional bodies and covering those who will form part of Public Health England and those with whom it will have close associations and wider professional networks.

5.10 Accountability for delivery in 2011/12 will continue to rest with SHAs and PCTs. In addition, SHAs will be responsible for the overall transition process in their regions during 2011/12. As part of this, Regional Directors of Public Health (RDsPH) will lead the transition for the public health system at the regional and local level.

5.11 The transition to Public Health England will be developed in alignment with changes to PCTs and SHAs, and the creation of the NHSCB. The detailed arrangements will be set out in a series of planning letters throughout the course of 2011.

2012/13 – consolidation

5.12 We envisage that Public Health England will come into being in April 2012 as an identifiable part of the Department of Health.

5.13 We will also publish shadow ring-fenced allocations for local authorities.

From April 2013 onwards

5.14 The new public health system will be in place. We will have implemented formal commissioning arrangements between Public Health England, the NHSCB, GP consortia and local authorities. The Department of Health will allocate ring-fenced budgets directly to upper-tier and unitary local authorities. Table 5.1 outlines the summary timetable.

Table 5.1: Summary timetable (subject to Parliamentary approval of legislation)	Date
Consultation on: • specific questions set out in this White Paper; • the public health outcomes framework; and • the funding and commissioning of public health.	Dec 2010–March 2011
Set up a shadow-form Public Health England within the Department of Health Start to set up working arrangements with local authorities, including the matching of PCT Directors of Public Health to local authority areas	During 2011
Develop the public health professional workforce strategy	Autumn 2011
Public Health England will take on full responsibilities, including the functions of the HPA and the NTA Publish shadow public health ring-fenced allocations to local authorities	April 2012
Grant ring-fenced allocations to local authorities	April 2013

Building on this White Paper

5.15 The Department of Health will publish a range of key documents throughout the year that link to this White Paper, including the following:

Winter 2010/11

- health visitors;

- mental health; and

- tobacco control.

Spring 2011

- Public Health Responsibility Deal;

- obesity;

- physical activity;

- social marketing;

- sexual health and teenage pregnancy; and

- pandemic flu.

Autumn 2011

- health protection, emergency preparedness and response.

5.16 Other government departments will also publish a range of documents that relate to public health and address the wider determinants of health, including:

- Child Poverty Strategy (HM Government);

- Drugs (HM Government);

- Public Services Reform White Paper (HM Government);

- Alcohol pricing and taxation (Her Majesty's Government);

- Crime Strategy (Home Office);

- Response to the consultation *Rebalancing the Licensing Act – on empowering individuals, families and local communities to shape and determine local licensing* (Home Office);

- Social Mobility White Paper (Cabinet Office);

- Welfare White Paper (Department for Work and Pensions);

- Special Educational Needs and Disability Green Paper (Department for Education);

- Munroe Review of Child Protection (Department for Education);

- Graham Allen Early Intervention Review (Department for Education);

- Local Transport White Paper (Department for Transport);

- Road Safety Strategy (Department for Transport);

- Natural Environment White Paper (Department for Environment, Food and Rural Affairs);

- Sentencing and Rehabilitation Green Paper (Ministry of Justice); and

- Skills Strategy (Department for Business, Innovation and Skills).

Consultation and engagement

5.17 To support ownership of the new public health system, in addition to existing engagement activity, the Department of Health will take forward work in partnership with relevant organisations, seeking their help and expertise in developing proposals that work in practice.

5.18 We will consult on the detailed design of the outcomes and funding frameworks set out in forthcoming consultation documents. We are also consulting on the specific questions in this White Paper, which are summarised overleaf.

Consultation questions

a. Role of GPs and GP practices in public health: Are there additional ways in which we can ensure that GPs and GP practices will continue to play a key role in areas for which Public Health England will take responsibility?

b. Public health evidence: What are the best opportunities to develop and enhance the availability, accessibility and utility of public health information and intelligence?

c. Public health evidence: How can Public Health England address current gaps such as using the insights of behavioural science, tackling wider determinants of health, achieving cost effectiveness, and tackling inequalities?

d. Public health evidence: What can wider partners nationally and locally contribute to improving the use of evidence in public health?

e. Regulation of public health professionals: We would welcome views on Dr Gabriel Scally's report. If we were to pursue voluntary registration, which organisation would be best suited to provide a system of voluntary regulation for public health specialists?

Forthcoming consultation documents will set out questions on the proposed public health outcomes framework and the funding and commissioning of public health.

5.19 We will arrange a programme of consultation and policy development events around England. Details will be posted on the Department of Health website, as well as advertised through stakeholder networks.

5.20 Consultation on the specific questions in this White Paper closes on 8 March 2011. You can contribute to the consultation by providing written comments:

by email to: publichealthengland@dh.gsi.gov.uk

by post to: Public Health Consultation
Department of Health
Room G13, Wellington House
133–155 Waterloo Road
London SE1 8UG

The consultation process

Criteria for consultation

5.21 The consultation on the questions set out above follows the Government Code of Practice on consultation. In particular we aim to:

- formally consult at a stage where there is scope to influence the policy outcome;

- consult for at least 12 weeks and consider longer timescales where feasible and sensible;

- be clear about the consultation's process in the consultation documents, what is being proposed, the scope to influence and the expected costs and benefits of the proposals;

- ensure that the consultation exercise is designed to be accessible to, and clearly targeted at, those people it is intended to reach;

- keep the burden of consultation to a minimum to ensure that consultations are effective and to obtain consultees' buy-in to the process;

- analyse responses carefully and give clear feedback to participants following the consultation; and

- ensure that the officials running the consultations are guided in how to run an effective consultation exercise and share what they learn from the experience.

5.22 The full text of the Code of Practice is on the Better Regulation website at:

www.bis.gov.uk/policies/better-regulation/consultation-guidance

Comments on the consultation process itself

5.23 If you have concerns or comments that you would like to make relating specifically to the consultation process itself please contact:

Consultations Co-ordinator
Department of Health
3E48, Quarry House
Leeds LS2 7UE

email: consultations.co-ordinator@dh.gsi.gov.uk

Please do not send consultation responses to this address.

Confidentiality of information

5.24 We manage the information you provide in response to this consultation in accordance with the Department of Health's Information Charter.[107]

5.25 Information we receive, including personal information, may be published or disclosed in accordance with the access to information regimes (primarily the Freedom of Information Act 2000 (FOIA), the Data Protection Act 1998 (DPA) and the Environmental Information Regulations 2004).

5.26 If you want the information that you provide to be treated as confidential, please be aware that, under the FOIA, there is a statutory Code of Practice with which public authorities must comply and which deals, among other things, with obligations of confidence. In view of this, it would be helpful if you could explain to us why you regard the information you have provided as confidential. If we receive a request for disclosure of the information we will take full account of your explanation, but we cannot give an assurance that confidentiality can be maintained in all circumstances. An automatic confidentiality disclaimer generated by your IT system will not, of itself, be regarded as binding on the Department.

5.27 The Department will process your personal data in accordance with the DPA and, in most circumstances, this will mean that your personal data will not be disclosed to third parties.

Summary of the consultation

5.28 A summary of the response to the consultation questions in this White Paper and forthcoming consultations on the proposed public health outcomes framework and the funding and commissioning of public health will be made available before or alongside any further action (such as laying legislation before Parliament), and will be placed on the consultations website at:

www.dh.gov.uk/en/Consultations/Responsestoconsultations/index.htm

Annex: A vision of the role of the Director of Public Health

1.   This Annex sets out a vision for the role of the Director of Public Health (DPH) developed in discussions between the Department of Health and public health professionals, local government and the NHS over recent months. DsPH have a critical leadership role in the new system – at the centre of improving the health and wellbeing of local communities across England.[i] This role is subject to passage of the Health and Social Care Bill.

Principal adviser

2.   We envisage that the DPH will be the principal adviser on all health matters to the local authority, its elected members and officers, on the full range of local authority functions and their impact on the health of the local population, including identifying health inequalities and developing and implementing local strategies to reduce them.

3.   He or she will be play a key role in the proposed new functions of local authorities in promoting integrated working; contribute to the development of the local Joint Strategic Needs Assessment (JSNA) and the joint health and wellbeing strategy; be an advocate for the public's health within the community; and produce an authoritative independent annual report on the health of their local population.

Provision and use of evidence

4.   The DPH will be responsible for ensuring that the local authority, and its key partners, have access to the high-quality analysis and evidence needed to inform the JSNA, the Annual Health Report, emergency preparation and response, and all public health services for which they are responsible. In tight financial times, it will be incumbent only to support effective interventions that deliver proven benefits, and to evaluate innovative approaches.

Population healthcare

5.   Although the DPH will be employed by local authorities, it will be vital to ensure a high-quality public health input into NHS services. DsPH will need to work closely with GPconsortia to help identify, prevent and manage a range of conditions, such as mental ill health, cardiovascular disease, diabetes and cancer, across the population, to support people to take care of their own health,

---

i   This includes Service personnel, their families and veterans.

promoting independence, self-care and self-management. DsPH will also need to have input into commissioning services for people with established diseases and long-term conditions, supported by high-quality community services provided by a wide range of health professionals.

6.   In addition to offering support to GP commissioners, the DPH will wish to engage in a range of regular informal and formal mechanisms for public health experts to advise other NHS colleagues. The DPH will work with NHS colleagues locally in:

   • advising on commissioning and effective operation of population health services;

   • ensuring the provision of services for diverse and potentially excluded groups (for example, people with mental health problems and with learning disabilities; the homeless; people in prisons and ex-offenders; children with special educational needs or disability and looked after children; and travellers);

   • advising on how to ensure equal access and equity of outcome across the population; and

   • working with and supporting health and social care colleagues to increase opportunities for using contacts with the public and service users to influence behaviours positively and thereby improve health.

Health protection and emergency preparedness and response

7.   Where the Secretary of State enters into arrangements with local authorities in relation to health protection and emergency preparedness, we envisage that the DPH will play an important role in local emergency planning and response to public health threats that affect their communities. They will be supported in this by the Health Protection Units (HPUs), which will provide specialist advice and access to the national resources of the public health service.

8.   DsPH will work closely with local HPUs across the full range of health protection issues and ensure they are appropriately reflected in the Annual Health Report and the JSNA and that co-ordinated action can be taken where necessary.

9.   The 'proper officer' for the purposes of the Public Health (Control of Disease) Act 1984 will continue to be appointed by the local authority (at the lower tier in a two-tier regime).

10.   Authorities (including port health authorities) will continue to provide health protection interventions according to existing legislation such as the Public Health (Control of Disease) Act 1984, Food Safety Act 1990, Environmental Protection Act 1990 and others.

11. DsPH and HPUs will contribute to Local Resilience Forums according to local need and expertise. DsPH will ensure that there are sufficient qualified and appropriately trained public health staff to maintain a robust and resilient on-call rota for major incidents, infectious disease outbreaks and port health at the local level.

12. DsPH and HPUs will work together to undertake local horizon scanning and risk management, health surveillance and, working with local partners, will develop plans and mitigation strategies for the threats and hazards that might affect health – supported by Public Health England as appropriate.

13. Local and National Resilience Forums will continue to play a vital role, working together with a range of organisations to ensure that we are prepared for and can respond to significant threats and emergencies.

Health improvement and inequalities

14. The DPH will be responsible for health improvement, addressing local inequalities in health outcomes, and addressing the wider determinants of health. He or she will work in partnership with other local government colleagues, and partners such as GP consortia, the wider NHS, early years services, schools, business, voluntary organisations and the police, to achieve better public health outcomes for the whole of their local population. This may also include working with other DsPH and Public Health England across a wider geographical area as appropriate. We would expect this to include personal public health services such as smoking cessation, alcohol brief interventions, weight management and work to address the wider determinants of health.

Accountability

15. DsPH will have a professional duty to keep their skills up to date and to ensure their staff are similarly well trained. This is to ensure there is a competent local multi-disciplinary public health workforce, with strong professional leadership at its heart.

16. The primary accountability for local government will be to their local populations through transparency of progress against outcomes and their local strategy. There will also be a relationship between Public Health England and local councils through the allocation of the ring-fenced budget, for which the Chief Executive will be the Accountable Officer; through transparency of progress against the outcomes framework; and through the incentives available to reward progress against health improvement outcomes.

17.   DsPH will be jointly appointed by the relevant local authority and Public Health England. While councils will have the power to dismiss DsPHs for serious failings across the full spectrum of their responsibilities, the Secretary of State for Health will have the power to dismiss them for serious failings in the discharge of their health protection functions. They will be accountable to the Secretary of State for Health and professionally accountable to the Chief Medical Officer.

Glossary

Commissioning – the process of assessing the needs of a local population and putting in place services to meet those needs.

Devolved Administrations – refers to the governments of Scotland (the Scottish Government), Wales (the National Assembly for Wales) and Northern Ireland (the Northern Ireland Assembly).

Directors of Public Health (DsPH) – currently a role within NHS primary care trusts, moving to local authorities in the future; the lead public health professionals who focus on protecting and improving the health of the local population.

Health and Social Care Bill – proposals for a Health Bill were included in the Queen's Speech for the first Parliamentary session of the Coalition Government. The Health and Social Care Bill will bring forward the legislative changes required for the implementation of the proposals in this White Paper.

Health premium – a component of the new funding mechanism for public health that will reflect deprivation and reward progress against health improvement outcomes in local areas.

Health Protection Agency (HPA) – the current non-departmental public body responsible for a range of health protection functions.

Local authorities – see **Local government**, below.

Local government – refers collectively to administrative authorities for local areas within England, with different arrangements in different areas, including:

- two-tier authorities: several district councils ('lower-tier', responsible for, for example, council housing, leisure services, recycling, etc.) overlap with a single county council ('upper-tier', responsible for, for example, schools, social services and public transport);

- unitary: a single layer of administration responsible for local public services, including: metropolitan district councils; boroughs; and city, county or district councils;

- town and parish councils: cover a smaller area than district councils and are responsible for, for example, allotments, public toilets, parks and ponds, war memorials, local halls and community centres; and

- shared services: where it is considered appropriate, local government may share services across areas greater than individual administrative bodies, for example, for policing, fire services and public transport.

Local Resilience Forum – a multi-agency partnership in a local area of Category 1 Responders (for example, emergency services, local authorities and the NHS), as defined by the Civil Contingencies Act 2004, often working closely with Category 2 responders (for example, the Highways Agency and public utility companies); responsible for establishing and maintaining arrangements to respond to major emergencies.

National Institute for Health and Clinical Excellence (NICE) – an independent organisation which provides advice and guidelines on the cost and effectiveness of drugs and treatments.

National Treatment Agency for Substance Misuse (NTA) – current special health authority established to improve the availability, capacity and effectiveness of treatment for drug misuse in England.

NHS Constitution – describes the principles and values of the NHS in England, and the rights and responsibilities of patients, the public and staff.

NHS Operating Framework – sets out the priorities for the NHS, the business rules to support their delivery and the accountability process for each financial year.

Primary care trust (PCT) – the NHS body currently responsible for commissioning healthcare services – and, in most cases, providing community-based services such as district nursing – for a local area.

Provider – an organisation that provides services directly to patients, including hospitals, mental health services and ambulance services.

Public Health Observatories – existing organisations that serve the public health intelligence needs of different regions in England.

Spending Review – set out the Government's priorities, and spending plans to meet these priorities, for the period 2011/12–2014/15.

Strategic health authorities (SHAs) – the 10 public bodies which currently oversee the commissioning and provision of NHS services at a regional level.

Unitary authority – see **Local government**, above.

Upper-tier authority –see **Local government**, above.

Endnotes

1. Marmot, M. (2010) *Fair Society, Healthy Lives: Strategic Review of Health Inequalities in England post 2010*, www.marmotreview.org

2. Department of Health (2010) *A Vision for Adult Social Care: Capable Communities and Active Citizens*, www.dh.gov.uk/en/Publicationsandstatistics/Publications/PublicationsPolicyAndGuidance/DH_121508

3. Department of Health (2010) *Equity and Excellence: Liberating the NHS*, www.dh.gov.uk/en/Healthcare/LiberatingtheNHS/index.htm

4. Black, C. (2008) *Dame Carol Black's Review of the Health of Britain's Working Age Population. Working for a Healthier Tomorrow*, www.dwp.gov.uk/docs/hwwb-working-for-a-healthier-tomorrow.pdf

5. Ibid.

6. Griffiths, S., Jewell, T. and Donnelly, P. (2005) Public health in practice: The three domains of public health. *Public Health*; 119(10): 907–13.

7. Office for National Statistics (2009) *Mortality Statistics: Deaths Registered in 2009*. www.statistics.gov.uk/downloads/theme_health/dr2009/dr-09.pdf

8. Callum, C. (2008) *The Cost of Smoking to the NHS*.

9. NHS Information Centre (2010) *Statistics on NHS Stop Smoking Services: England, April 2009 – March 2010*, www.ic.nhs.uk/pubs/SSS0910

10. See Department of Health (2010) *Our Health and Wellbeing Today* for further examples.

11. Office for National Statistics (2010) *Life Expectancy at Birth and at Age 65 by Local Areas in the United Kingdom, 2007–09*, www.statistics.gov.uk/pdfdir/liex1010.pdf

12. Office for National Statistics (2008) *Period and cohort life expectancy tables 2008* http://www.statistics.gov.uk/statbase/product.asp?vlnk=15098

13. Office for National Statistics (2009) *Mortality Statistics: Deaths Registered in 2009*, www.statistics.gov.uk/downloads/theme_health/dr2009/dr-09.pdf

14. Ibid.

15. Department of Health analysis of *General Household Survey/General Lifestyle Survey* data, Office for National Statistics, 1980–2009, www.statistics.gov.uk/statbase/product.asp?vlnk=5756

16. Department of Health analysis, Health Survey England 2006 data.

17. Office for National Statistics (2007) *General Household Survey 2007*, www.statistics.gov.uk/statbase/prep/5756.asp

18. Eurofound (2007) *European Quality of Life Survey 2007*, www.eurofound.europa.eu/areas/qualityoflife/eqls/2007/index.htm

19. Marmot, M. (2010) *Fair Society, Healthy Lives: Strategic Review of Health Inequalities in England post 2010*, www.marmotreview.org

20. Disability Rights Commission (2006) *Equal treatment – closing the gap*; Mencap (2007) *Death by indifference*; Sir Jonathan Michael (2008) *Healthcare for all: report of the independent inquiry into access to healthcare for people with learning disabilities*, DH; Local Government Ombudsman and Parliamentary & Health Service Ombudsman (2009) *Six lives: the provision of public services to people with learning disabilities*.

21. Cemlyn S, et al (2009), *Inequalities experienced by Gypsy and Traveller communities: A review*. Equalities and Human Rights Commission http://www.equalityhumanrights.com/uploaded_files/research/12inequalities_experienced_by_gypsy_and_traveller_communities_a_review.pdf

22. Bunker, J. (2001). *Medicine Matters After All: Measuring the Benefits of Medical care, a Healthy Lifestyle, and a Just Social Environment.*

23. Hall, J.A. and Valente, T.W. (2007) Adolescent smoking networks: The effects of influence and selection on future smoking. *Journal of Addictive Behaviour*; 32(12): 3054–9. Achat, H., Kawachi, I., Levine, S. et al. (1998) Social networks, stress and health-related quality of life. *Quality of Life Research*; 7(8): 735–50.

24. Christakis, N.A. and Fowler, J.H. (2009) *Connected: The Surprising Power of Our Social Networks and How They Shape Our Lives*, Little, Brown and Company.

25. O'Hara, M.W. and Swain, A.M. (1996) Rates and risk of postpartum depression – a meta-analysis, *International review of psychiatry*; 8(1): 37-54.

26. Hay, D.F., Pawlby, S., Sharp, D. et al. (2001) Intellectual problems shown by 11-year-old children whose mothers had postnatal depression. *Journal of Child Psychology and Psychiatry, and Allied Disciplines*; 42(7): 871–89.

27. Ibid.

28. Department of Health (2010) *Health Profile of England 2009*, www.dh.gov.uk/en/Publicationsandstatistics/Publications/PublicationsStatistics/DH_114561. Data updated to 2009 from the Office for National Statistics website at www.statistics.gov.uk/downloads/theme_health/infant-perinatal-mortality-summary-tables.xls

29. Gray, R., Headley, J., Oakley, L. et al. (2009) *Inequalities in Infant Mortality Project Briefing Paper 3. Towards an understanding of variations in infant mortality rates between different ethnic groups in England and Wales*, www.npeu.ox.ac.uk/files/downloads/infant-mortality/Infant-Mortality-Briefing-Paper-3.pdf; Kurinczuk, J., Hollowell, J., Brocklehurst, P and Gray, R. (2009) *Inequalities in Infant Mortality Project Briefing Paper 1 Infant mortality: overview and context* www.npeu.ox.ac.uk/files/downloads/infant-mortality/Infant-Mortality-Briefing-Paper-1.pdf

30. Heslehurst, N., Ells, L.J., Simpson, H. et al. (2007) Trends in maternal obesity incidence rates, demographic predictors, and health inequalities in 36 821 women over a 15-year period. *BJOG: An International Journal of Obstetrics and Gynaecology*; 114(2): 187–94.

31. Department of Health (2010) *Statistical Release: Breastfeeding Initiation and Prevalence at 6–8 Weeks, Q2 2010/11*, www.dh.gov.uk/en/Publicationsandstatistics/Publications/PublicationsStatistics/DH_116060

32. NHS Information Centre (2006) *Infant Feeding Survey 2005: Early Results*, www.ic.nhs.uk/pubs/breastfeed2005

33. Gray, R., Bonellie, S.R., Chalmers, J. et al. (2009) Contribution of smoking during pregnancy to inequalities in stillbirth and infant death in Scotland 1994–2003: Retrospective population based study using hospital maternity records. *British Medical Journal*; 339: b3754.

34. Department of Health (2007) *Implementation Plan for Reducing Health Inequalities in Infant Mortality: A Good Practice Guide*, www.dh.gov.uk/en/Publicationsandstatistics/Publications/PublicationsPolicyAndGuidance/DH_081337

35. World Health Organization Regional Office for Europe, Health for all database, data from 2001, http://data.euro.who.int/hfadb/

36. Kramer, M.S., Sèguin, L., Lydon, J. and Goulet, L. (2000) Socio-economic disparities in pregnancy outcome: Why do the poor fare so poorly? *Paediatric and Perinatal Epidemiology*; 14(3): 194–210.

37. Green, H., McGinnity, A., Meltzer, H. et al. (2005) *Mental Health of Children and Young People in Great Britain, 2004*, www.statistics.gov.uk/downloads/theme_health/GB2004.pdf

38. Richards, M. and Abbott, R. (2009) *Childhood Mental Health and Life Chances in Post-War Britain: Insights from Three National Birth Cohort Studies*, www.centreformentalhealth.org.uk/pdfs/life_chances_report.pdf

39. Department for Transport (2010) *Reported Road Casualties Great Britain 2009: Annual Report*, www.dft.gov.uk/pgr/statistics/datatablespublications/accidents/casualtiesgbar/rrcgb2009

40. National Obesity Observatory (2010) *National Child Measurement Programme: Changes in Children's Body Mass Index between 2006/07 and 2008/09*, www.noo.org.uk/uploads/doc/vid_6540_NOO_NCMP_v1.pdf

41. Rudolf, M. (2009) *Tackling Obesity through the Healthy Child Programme: A Framework for Action*, www.noo.org.uk/uploads/doc/vid_4865_rudolf_TacklingObesity1_210110.pdf

42. National Obesity Observatory (2010) *National Child Measurement Programme: Changes in Children's Body Mass Index between 2006/07 and 2008/09*, www.noo.org.uk/uploads/doc/vid_6540_NOO_NCMP_v1.pdf

43. Hall, J.A. and Valente, T.W. (2007) Adolescent smoking networks: The effects of influence and selection on future smoking. *Journal of Addictive Behaviour*; 32(12): 2054-9. Achat, H., Kawachi, I., Levine, S. et al. (1998) Social networks, stress and health-related quality of life. *Quality of Life Research*; 7(8): 735-50.

44. Hoare, J. and Moon, D. (ed.) (2010) *Home Office Statistical Bulletin 13/10. Drug Misuse Declared: Findings from the 2009/10 British Crime Survey, England and Wales*, http://rds.homeoffice.gov.uk/rds/pdfs10/hosb1310.pdf

45. Health Protection Agency (2010) Sexually Transmitted Infections, Annual Data Table 2009, www.hpa.org.uk/Topics/InfectiousDiseases/InfectionsAZ/STIs/STIsAnnualData/

46. Organisation for Economic Co-operation and Development (OECD) (2009) *Doing Better for Children*, www.oecd.org/document/12/0,3343,en_2649_34819_43545036_1_1_1_37419,00.html

47. Kessler, R.C., Berglund, P., Demler, O. et al. (2005) *Lifetime prevalence and age-of-onset distributions of DSM-IV disorders in the National Comorbidity Survey replication.* Archives of General Psychiatry; 62(6): 593–602;
Kim-Cohen, J., Caspi, A., Moffitt, T.E. et al. (2003) *Prior juvenile diagnoses in adults with mental disorder: Developmental follow-back of a prospective-longitudinal cohort.* Archives of General Psychiatry; 60(7): 709–17.

48. Robinson, S. and Bugler, C. (2010) *General Lifestyle Survey 2008. Smoking and Drinking among Adults, 2008*, www.statistics.gov.uk/downloads/theme_compendia/GLF08/GLFSmoking&DrinkingAmongAdults2008.pdf

49. Whitaker, R.C., Wright, J.A., Pepe, M.S. et al. (1997) Predicting obesity in young adulthood from childhood and parental obesity. *New England Journal of Medicine*; 337(13): 869–73.

50. NHS Information Centre (2009) *Statistics on Alcohol: England, 2009*, www.ic.nhs.uk/webfiles/publications/alcoholeng2009/Final%20Format%20draft%202009%20v7.pdf

51. Jones, L., Bellis, M.A., Dedman, D. et al. (2008) *Alcohol-attributable Fractions for England: Alcohol-attributable Mortality and Hospital Admissions*, www.alcohollearningcentre.org.uk/_library/AlcoholAttributableFractions.pdf

52. Boyle, P., Autier, P., Bartelink, H. (2003) European Code Against Cancer and scientific justification: third version (2003). *Annals of Oncology*; 14(7): 973–1005.

53. National Institute for Health and Clinical Excellence (2010) *Prevention of Cardiovascular Disease at the Population Level*, www.nice.org.uk/PH25

54. Robinson, S. and Bugler, C. (2010) *General Lifestyle Survey 2008. Smoking and Drinking among Adults, 2008*, www.statistics.gov.uk/downloads/theme_compendia/GLF08/GLFSmoking&DrinkingAmongAdults2008.pdf

55. Callum, C. (2008) *The Cost of Smoking to the NHS*.

56. NHS Information Centre (2009) *Health Survey for England 2008*, www.ic.nhs.uk/statistics-and-data-collections/health-and-lifestyles-related-surveys/health-survey-for-england

57. Government Office for Science (2007) *Tackling Obesity: Future Choices*, Foresight Report.

58. Food Standards Agency/Bates, B., Lennox, A. and Swan, G. (eds) (2010) *National Diet and Nutrition Survey: Headline Results from Year 1 of the Rolling Programme (2008/2009)*, www.food.gov.uk/multimedia/pdfs/publication/ndnsreport0809.pdf

59. Eastern Region Public Health Observatory (2008) *Modelled Estimates and Projections of Hypertension for PCTs in England*, www.erpho.org.uk/viewResource.aspx?id=17905

60. Food Standards Agency/Bates, B., Lennox, A. and Swan, G. (eds) (2010) *National Diet and Nutrition Survey: Headline Results from Year 1 of the Rolling Programme (2008/2009)*, www.food.gov.uk/multimedia/pdfs/publication/ndnsreport0809.pdf

61. Self-reported data from NHS Information Centre (2009) *Health Survey for England 2008*, www.ic.nhs.uk/statistics-and-data-collections/health-and-lifestyles-related-surveys/health-survey-for-england

62. Office for National Statistics (2008). *Smoking and Drinking among Adults, 2008, from the General Lifestyle Survey*, www.statistics.gov.uk/downloads/theme_compendia/GLF08/GLFSmoking&DrinkingAmongAdults2008.pdf

63. Gil-González, D., Vives-Cases, C., Álvarez-Dardet, C. and Latour-Pérez, J. (2006) Alcohol and intimate partner violence: Do we have enough information to act? *European Journal of Public Health*; 16(3): 278–84.

64. Hoare, J. and Moon, D. (ed.) (2010) *Home Office Statistical Bulletin 13/10. Drug Misuse Declared: Findings from the 2009/10 British Crime Survey, England and Wales*, http://rds.homeoffice.gov.uk/rds/pdfs10/hosb1310.pdf

65. Health Protection Agency (2010) *Sexually Transmitted Infections, Annual Data Table 2009*, www.hpa.org.uk/Topics/InfectiousDiseases/InfectionsAZ/STIs/STIsAnnualData/

66. Health Protection Agency (2010) *HIV in the United Kingdom: 2010 Report*.

67. Department of Health analysis, Health Survey England 2006 data.

68. World Health Organisation (2004) *Global burden of disease statistics – 2004 data*

69. SCMH (2003). *Policy Paper 3: The Economic and Social Costs of Mental Illness*. London: The Sainsbury Centre for Mental Health.

70. NHS Information Centre (2009) *Adult Psychiatric Morbidity Survey 2007*, www.ic.nhs.uk/pubs/psychiatricmorbidity07

71. NHS Information Centre for health and social care, *Adult Psychiatric Morbidity Survey 2007* http://www.ic.nhs.uk/pubs/psychiatricmorbidity07

72. Brown, S., Kim, M., Mitchell, C. and Inskip, H. (2010) Twenty-five year mortality of a community cohort with schizophrenia. *British Journal of Psychiatry*; 196(2): 116–21.

73. Carers UK (2004) *In Poor Health: The Impact of Caring on Health*, www.carersuk.org/Professionals/ResearchLibrary/Healthandcare/1201185222

74. Black, C. (2008) *Dame Carol Black's Review of the Health of Britain's Working Age Population. Working for a Healthier Tomorrow,* www.dwp.gov.uk/docs/hwwb-working-for-a-healthier-tomorrow.pdf

75. Ibid.

76. Ibid.

77. Department for Work and Pensions Information Directorate: Work and Pensions Longitudinal Study.

78. Health and Safety Executive (2010) Health and Safety Statistics 2009/10, www.hse.gov.uk/

79. Office for National Statistics (2010) *Life Expectancy at Birth and at Age 65 by Local Areas in the United Kingdom, 2007–09*, www.statistics.gov.uk/pdfdir/liex1010.pdf

80. Social Exclusion Task Force (2009) *Working Together for Older People in Rural Areas*, www.cabinetoffice.gov.uk/media/226170/working-together-older-people-rural-areas-july09.pdf

81. King's College London and the London School of Economics for the Alzheimer's Society (2007) *Dementia UK*, http://alzheimers.org.uk/site/scripts/download_info.php?fileID=2; Health Economics Research Centre for the Alzheimer's Research Trust (2010) Dementia 2010, www.dementia2010.org

82. Department of Health (2007) *National Dementia Strategy*, www.dh.gov.uk/en/SocialCare/NationalDementiaStrategy/index.htm

83. Godfrey, M., Townsend, J., Surr, C. et al. (2005) *Prevention and Service Provision: Mental Health Problems in Later Life*. NHS Information Centre (2007) *Health Survey for England 2005: Health of Older People*, www.ic.nhs.uk/pubs/hse05olderpeople

84. Age Concern/Help the Aged (2009) *One Voice: Shaping our Ageing Society*; Scharf, T. et al. (2002) *Growing Older in Socially Deprived Areas: Social Exclusion in Later Life*.

85. Office for National Statistics (2010) *Life Expectancy at Birth and at Age 65 by Local Areas in the United Kingdom, 2007–09*, www.statistics.gov.uk/pdfdir/liex1010.pdf

86. Office for National Statistics excess winter deaths statistics, www.statistics.gov.uk/statbase/Product.asp?vlnk=10805

87. Green, G. and Gilbertson, J. for the Warm Front Study Group (2008) *Warm Front Better Health: Health Impact Evaluation of the Warm Front Scheme*, www.apho.org.uk/resource/view.aspx?RID=53281

88. National Institute for Health and Clinical Excellence (2004) *Clinical Practice Guidelines for the Assessment and Prevention of Falls in Older People*, www.nice.org.uk/CG21

89. Hospital Episode Statistics data, www.hesonline.nhs.uk

90. NHS Information Centre (2010) *The National Hip Fracture Database: National Report 2010*, www.rcseng.ac.uk/news/docs/NHFD%20(final).pdf

91. Department of Health (2010) *Transparency in Outcomes – A Framework for the NHS*, www.dh.gov.uk/en/Consultations/Closedconsultations/DH_117583

92. Department of Health (2010). *A Consultation on Proposals – Transparency in Outcomes: A Framework for Adult Social Care*, www.dh.gov.uk/en/Consultations/Liveconsultations/DH_121509. Consultation open until 9 February 2011.

93. Reeves, R. for the Department of Health (2010) *A Liberal Dose? Health and Wellbeing: The Role of the State*, www.dh.gov.uk/en/Publicationsandstatistics/Publications/PublicationsPolicyAndGuidance/DH_111697

94. Based on 'the intervention ladder' described in the Nuffield Council on Bioethics report (2007) *Public health: ethical issues*

95. Marmot, M. (2010) *Fair Society, Healthy Lives: Strategic Review of Health Inequalities in England post 2010*, www.marmotreview.org p.126.

96. Ibid.

97. Thaler, R.H., and Sunstain, C.R. (2008) *Nudge: Improving decisions about health, wealth and happiness*; Institute for government and Cabinet Office (2010) *MINDSPACE Influencing behaviour through public policy*; Hardistry and Weber (2009) Discounting future green: money versus the environment. *Journal of Experimental Psychology: general* 138(3): 329-340.

98. Marmot, M. (2010) *Fair Society, Healthy Lives: Strategic Review of Health Inequalities in England post 2010*, www.marmotreview.org

99. Department for the Environment, Food and Rural Affairs (2010) *Noise Policy Statement for England* www.defra.gov.uk/environment/quality/noise/policy/index.htm

100. HM Government (2010) *Call to end violence against women and girls* http://www.homeoffice.gov.uk/publications/crime/call-end-violence-women-girls/

101. Department of Health (2010) *Improving services for women and child victims of violence: the Department of Health Action Plan*, http://www.dh.gov.uk/en/ Publicationsandstatistics/Publications/PublicationsPolicyAndGuidance/DH_122003

102. Black, C. (2008) *Dame Carol Black's Review of the Health of Britain's Working Age Population. Working for a Healthier Tomorrow*, www.dwp.gov.uk/docs/hwwb-workingfor-a-healthier-tomorrow.pdf

103. Callum, C. (2008) *The Cost of Smoking to the NHS.*

104. HM Government (2010) *The Coalition: our programme for government* http://www.cabinetoffice.gov.uk/media/409088/pfg_coalition.pdf

105. http://data.gov.uk/blog/new-public-sector-transparency-board-and-public-data-transparency-principles

106. The National Institute for Health and Clinical Excellence has developed a way to conduct cost impact and return on investment calculations to accompany its public health and social care guidance and quality standards. This could provide the basis for decision making and priority setting at a local level by GP consortia and local authorities, enabling effective commissioning by Directors of Public Health: www.nice. org.uk/ourguidance/otherpublications/costimpactinvestmentreturn.jsp

107. www.dh.gov.uk/en/FreedomOfInformation/DH_088010

© Crown copyright 2010
403161 1p 500 November 2010 (PC)
Produced by COI for the Department of Health